Pelican Books
Population Control

25p.

G000067214

Edited by Anthony Allison

Population
Control

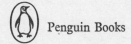 Penguin Books

Penguin Books Ltd, Harmondsworth,
Middlesex, England
Penguin Books Inc., 7110 Ambassador Road,
Baltimore, Maryland 21207, U.S.A.
Penguin Books Australia Ltd, Ringwood,
Victoria, Australia

First published 1970
Copyright © Penguin Books Ltd, 1970

Made and printed in Great Britain by
Cox & Wyman Ltd, London, Reading and Fakenham
Set in Monotype Plantin

Contents

Introduction

The general theme of this volume is 'Population Growth and Control', which is one of the major problems facing contemporary biologists. The explosion of human populations, like The Bomb, is a shadow hanging over us all during the second half of the twentieth century – a shadow which has itself arisen as a result of scientific achievements. Human population growth has implications in many different fields, from the biology of fertility control to sociology and economics. We have obtained contributions on many of these problems by experts. In an attempt to place the human problems in a general biological perspective, essays are included on population growth and control in other animals and plants. Such observations are of interest in their own right and have varying degrees of relevance to the human situation.

Rosemary Reid opens with an essay on protozoan populations, which can be taken as representative of certain kinds of problems posed by populations of unicellular organisms. In a pure culture of a bacterium or protozoon, population density increase usually follows a characteristic pattern: after an initial lag the organisms increase logarithmically until absence of a dietary requirement or some other factor limits growth. The organisms cease to multiply and a stationary phase continues until the organisms are sub-cultured or die out. When two or more organisms are cultured together, the resulting populations differ widely depending on the particular experimental conditions. The final population may consist entirely or predominantly of one organism, or may be mixed. Similarly complex relationships are found in natural populations of protozoa. Some of the examples discussed by Dr Reid, such as those in sewage, have relevance to water recovery and pollution, which is an increasingly important practical problem in the overcrowded industrial areas of our planet. Others, such as the still mysterious fluctuations in populations of marine plankton, are reflected in the size of fish populations.

J. L. Harper's chapter on population biology in plants again emphasizes the complexity of the interactions determining population densities under natural conditions. However, well-controlled experiments are sometimes possible and have yielded clear-cut results. These can have important practical implications, as in density dependence of crop yields, growth of weeds, and long-term effects of selective herbicides. Appropriate to the implications of this volume is the definition of life as an existentialist game in which success is measured by continuing to play the game.

H. G. Andrewartha outlines the principles affecting growth and control of animal populations, and quotes examples of each in action. Often the effects of controlling agents are density-dependent, as might be expected from first principles – for food, predators, and so forth. But quite often such factors operate independently of the density of the population. There is too little evidence to assess unambiguously the relative importance of these several mechanisms in limiting the density of natural populations of most animal species. But there is general agreement that if the density-dependent checks known to affect lower animals were to operate on human populations there would be much misery. Hence the need for density-independent restraints on human population growth.

The fourth chapter, by Christopher Perrins, is on bird populations. With most birds death rates are high, and old age is not an important factor contributing to mortality. Rate of reproduction varies markedly from species to species. The balance of evidence favours the view that birds are breeding as fast as they can without damaging the prospects of survival of their young. With most birds losses due to natural catastrophes such as severe winters, or to shooting or other forms of human intervention, affect numbers only temporarily; restoration to about the previous number takes place quite quickly. However, loss of a particular habitat or breeding place, or hunting of some slow-breeding species, such as birds of prey, can lead to extinction of particular species, and this is a matter for international concern.

Factors affecting natural populations of large mammals, especially game animals, are discussed by Leslie Brown. Even the more obvious controlling factors – such as intensity of predation, disease, and food supply – are seldom easily quantified, and in recent years attention has been given to other forms of population control, such as the existence of behavioural or reproductive patterns that are adapted to population density. Fortunately, many species seem to be able to survive even when they are hunted in part of their territory, but some are, of course, in danger of extinction. This is a matter for international concern and action.

The relationship of animal behaviour to population density has been extensively studied by John B. Calhoun. He has shown that when rats in experimental breeding colonies increase in numbers beyond a certain limit, their behaviour becomes erratic and deteriorates: they become aggressive, and the females do not clean their nests or look after their young properly. These observations on the development of 'population sinks' as a result of overcrowding attracted widespread attention because it seemed that they might have some analogy with behaviour of human populations in slum conditions. Some recent developments suggest that the maximum density that a mouse colony can attain is dependent on the number of individuals used to found the colony, and Calhoun speculates on the interpretation of these and other observations in relation to needs for space.

The contributions on human populations begin with a reminder from W. Brass of the nature of the growth of world population. He emphasizes how unreliable forecasts have been in the past and are still likely to be. Whatever range of estimates we take, projected growth rates and population sizes are formidable. The prospects are particularly frightening for the poorer regions of the world. By the end of the century these countries will contain nearly 80 per cent of a world population of more than 7,000,000,000. This must be viewed in terms of the widening gap in rates of economic development in privileged and under-privileged societies.

The relationship of population growth to food supplies is discussed by Ester Boserup. She emphasizes once again how difficult it is to predict what the increases in food production are likely to be, quite apart from factors such as political instability. However, a cautiously optimistic viewpoint can be taken. There are possibilities for improvement of subsistence agriculture, although a more widespread revolution in agricultural practices is necessary to make any great impact. The consequences of foreign aid to food production and of food importation can sometimes be unexpected. The lessons of the past two decades should be of some help in shaping future policies.

We then turn to the limitation of human population expansion. Burton Benedict discusses factors regulating populations in primitive societies. Precise information is scanty, but it seems likely that, except under unusually severe conditions, populations are not regulated by the available food supply but according to the prestige associated with having children. This, of course, varies greatly in different societies and changes with altered social patterns of behaviour, in particular urbanization. But in rural societies attitudes to childbearing can be remarkably persistent.

Ruth (Fowler) and Robert Edwards describe the contraceptive methods now available, their advantages, and their limitations. It is surprising how much is still unknown, e.g. why continuous administration of low doses of certain progestins prevents conception. Although there have been important developments, the perfect contraceptive has not yet been found. This field, and even more so the question of legalizing abortions, is heavily clouded with emotion, as the debates about the recent legislation in the United Kingdom suffice to show. But dissemination of accurate information does much to overcome ignorance, if not prejudice, and the Edwards' chapter usefully summarizes the present state of knowledge in this important field.

It is one thing to have effective contraceptive measures, but quite another to apply them on a wide scale. Colin Stewart reviews what is known of the scope and effectiveness of population limitation programmes in various countries. In some – notably Japan – these are being effective in holding down the birth rate; in most countries, even those that officially support population limitation (such as India and Pakistan), the actual effectiveness of the programmes has so far been limited. In Latin America and most African countries there is no official backing and private efforts are on a small scale.

The economic and social implications of population control are reviewed by Colin Clark. Like all the other aspects so far considered, the interaction of effects of income, occupation, and education on family size has proved to be complex and, in some measure, unpredictable. One important sociological difference is that between the extended family, involving many relations and children, and the nuclear family, in which income – and responsibilities – are shared by husband, wife, and children alone. In most parts of Africa and Asia the extended family is still the rule. Some consequences of population control are at first sight unexpected. When the economics of the community are considered as a whole – in the advanced countries at least – population growth is usually advantageous. Population increase can actually increase a country's savings. But this may not occur in an ageing population, and the necessity of doing something to decrease the gap between the economies of rich and poor nations needs no stressing.

Although the magnitude of the population problem is widely recognized, most people have come to accept it as a fact of life, and have largely ceased to think about it. That is why constant reminders of the situation are necessary, and we trust that this volume will contribute to that end. Much more could be done, especially by the advanced countries helping the poorer. Research on different methods of contraception is now progressing quite rapidly, although expenditure on research and development in this field is still low when compared with that on cancer, for example. In many countries this work has no official backing. A small fraction of the space research budget would make a large impact. We can only hope that rationality will prevail against prejudice and ignorance. Several contributors to this volume have emphasized that the most gloomy neo-Malthusian predictions are unjustified. There is room for expansion of agriculture, and some time to attempt to introduce new attitudes. But social and cultural inertia is immense, and only action in the next few decades on a large scale will prevent the Malthusian nightmare from eventually becoming a reality.

ANTHONY ALLISON

Protozoan Populations

Rosemary Reid

The Protozoa: What They Are and What They Do

The productivity of land and sea, and the health of human and animal populations are vitally affected by the activities of unicellular organisms called protozoa. Evolving within the boundaries set by the single cell and by a requirement for some water in the environment, the protozoa have colonized land, water, plants and animals with remarkable success. Over 50,000 protozoan species have been described. Some are no bigger than bacteria, others are visible with the naked eye. Protozoan populations can be found in clean and in polluted waters; in ponds and oceans; in acid bogs and salt lakes; in soil and sand; and parasitizing plants and animals.

Possibly the first reference to a protozoan population occurs in the Bible, since one of the ten plagues of Egypt in the story of Moses was probably the result of a huge increase in a population of red protozoa. This phenomenon, known as 'red water', is frequently seen in many oceans. The White Cliffs of Dover are massive visible evidence of the marine protozoa which lived in the oceans which covered the earth millions of years ago. The cliffs are formed, in part, from fossilized protozoan skeletons. The sea washing the foot of the cliffs teems with protozoa which live in the surface waters as part of the floating or swimming population of micro-organisms known as the plankton.

Complex communities of protozoa combine their activities with those of other micro-organisms – such as bacteria, algae, diatoms and fungi, collectively known as microflora – to maintain the fertility of soil, and to degrade natural and man-made wastes, dead organisms, sewage, and organic trade effluents, thus cleaning the environment and returning valuable nutrients to primary producers. Natural purification processes are exploited in waste treatment plants, where sewage and fluid trade wastes are passed through filters, aeration tanks, or oxygen ponds, populated by vast numbers of micro-organisms which feed on and degrade the wastes, the population in oxygen ponds consisting largely of algae and pigmented protozoa. The final effluent is sufficiently pure for discharge into adjacent natural waters. However, huge population increases ('blooms') of pigmented protozoa, induced by changing environmental conditions, cause bad odours and tastes in drinking water, pollute beaches with stinking slime if the blooms are washed up to die, and cause huge fishkills, if the bloom species secretes toxins, or the decomposition of blooms deoxygenates water, suffocating the fish.

Many protozoa live harmlessly on or in other animals, but some occasionally invade tissues, such species causing amoebic dysentery, vaginal inflammation, and abortion in cattle. Other protozoa are always pathogenic, the best known protozoan-caused diseases being malaria and African sleeping sickness.

Protozoan nutrition and habits: food-webs, fertility, and parasites.

Protozoan distribution and population density are determined by nutritional requirements and ranges of tolerance. Like bacteria, protozoa are in intimate contact with their environment, their cell walls being permeable to a variety of large and small molecules, and thus they respond rapidly to physico-chemical variations, which also modify food supply.

There is a remarkable variety of feeding habits among protozoa, ranging from osmotrophy in species which absorb simple chemicals from which they synthesize all their other requirements, to phagotrophy, in species which ingest and digest particulate food – cell fragments, rotting matter, or other organisms. Protozoa parasitizing vertebrate blood and cells have requirements rivalling those of their hosts due to parallel evolution.

Photosynthetic (autotrophic) species have the simplest requirements. These osmotrophs, like plants and photosynthetic microbes, contain pigment with which they trap energy from sunlight, incorporating it into the organic molecules they synthesize from water, carbon dioxide, and simple inorganic molecules. Autotrophic protozoa rank as primary producers in the food-webs which link the activities of plants and animals, photosynthesis introducing energy into biological systems bound into complex molecules which less dexterous organisms require, and releasing oxygen essential for non-photosynthetic (heterotrophic) species.

All other protozoa are heterotrophic, requiring organic food. They fall into two groups; the first, all free-living species and parasites of mouth and gut, co-exist with microflora; the second group being parasites of cells and body fluids, whose hosts supply organic requirements. Heterotrophs have lost many ancestral autotrophic synthetic mechanisms, due to evolution in environments where associated organisms supplied food, the most extreme examples of reduced biosynthetic capacity occurring in intracellular parasites. Osmotrophic heterotrophs are satisfied by dissolved food; intracellular phagotrophs take in cell fragments; phagotrophic mouth and gut parasites ingest particles of the hosts' diet, and gut microflora; saprophytic protozoa are scavengers, feeding on dissolved and solid products of decomposition; vegetarians prey on microflora, carnivores on other protozoa, some also attacking small invertebrates.

Few protozoa are restricted to a single feeding habit, extreme specialization making life hazardous. Probably all protozoa obtain some food from solution, and many autotrophs can resort to heterotrophic methods when light is restricted. Many predators are omnivorous, eating any prey they can trap and ingest. Parasites have the most specialized diets but do not have to hunt for food, being adapted for rapid transfer between hosts.

The habitat's dominant protozoa thus indicates its chemical and biological complexity. Autotrophs dominate in habitats with low organic content, such as streams running over hard rock. Fertile waters with plentiful oxygen and light support rich and varied microflora, reflected in the diversity of the protozoan fauna, which includes autotrophs and representatives of all heterotrophic habits. Parasitic sites are rich in organics, but food supply and physico-chemical conditions are highly specialized; hence they support dense but simple populations.

Variety of diet is reflected in diversity of physical specialization. Protozoa float, swim, creep, or are attached (sessile) on solids or vegetation. Floaters are predominantly osmotrophic; swimmers and sessile species are predatory; and creepers are predatory or saprophytic. Volume of fluid in the environment is related to the habit of the dominant population. Thus floaters dominate in blood, cells, and open waters; swimmers in waters rich with prey or particulate food; creepers and sessile species in habitats with plenty of substrate such as beds of aquatic environments, soil, sand, and the gut. Fluid movement is also significant, affecting population composition and maintenance. Strong currents as in fast-flowing streams, wash away planktonic (floating and swimming) species, but permit the establishment of some sessile and creeping species. Standing waters support both planktonic and benthic (bottom-dwelling) protozoa. Gut parasites are either creeping phagotrophs or are osmotrophs which attach to the gut lining. If species in habitats subjected to currents are not adapted to live in contact with solid surfaces, their reproductive rate must compensate for organisms washed away.

Protozoa reproduce by simple or multiple fission, many species having complicated life cycles combining both methods. Multiple fission is usually followed by sexual or dormant phases, but the products of simple fission can usually immediately begin to feed. Many protozoa can complete simple fission within an hour. Logarithmic increase of healthy populations permits rapid colonization of habitats when conditions are favourable. Protozoan taxonomy recognizes three main groups of species; flagellates, amoebae and ciliates, and a small but important fourth group – all intracellular parasites – the sporozoa. Protozoan morphology and life cycles are very varied. For the purposes of this discussion only the simplest outline is given. The reader is referred to publications cited at the end of the text for more detailed descriptions.

Flagellates have one or more whiplashes (flagella) which they use to pull or propel themselves about, or to keep afloat. Amoebae are very plastic, extending lobes or threads of protoplasm, (pseudopodia), for creeping or floating, and feeding. Ciliates have hair-like cilia on a greater or lesser area of the body, all except one group having a true mouth, the exceptions being suctorian ciliates, which have tentacles to trap and digest their prey. Swimming ciliates move by rhythmic beating of the felt of cilia covering the body; some creeping ciliates have legs of fused cilia; sessile species (except suctorians) have crowns of cilia which create a feeding current. Suctorians and other sessile ciliates produce ciliated larvae which swim to a new site, attach and develop into adults. Photosynthetic protozoa are flagellate, but some amoebae and ciliates harbour photosynthetic microbes which contribute to their hosts' nutrition. The saprophytic habit is characteristic of amoebae, but also occurs in the other two main groups. Ciliates are predatory, and many amoebae and flagellates are predators, trapping their prey with pseudopodia. Free-living and parasitic species occur in the three main groups, but most pathogenic protozoa are flagellates or sporozoa. The most important ciliate parasites are those living in the rumen of hoofed herbivores – cattle, goats, and sheep, for example – the ciliates making significant contributions to fodder digestion. The host lacks the requisite enzymes to digest the cellulose and other complex carbohydrates making up the bulk of the diet, and relies on the digestive activities of rumen microflora and protozoa. This mutually favourable host-parasite relationship is termed symbiosis; another example is the seething populations of gut flagellates in wood-eating termites.

Physico-chemical conditions controlling population distribution, density, and composition. The activity of protozoa, and the quality and quantity of their food, are related, and modified, by physico-chemical factors, sometimes termed abiotic (non-living) factors. These include: temperature; light intensity; concentration of gases (oxygen, carbon dioxide, and the toxic gas hydrogen sulphide, released during bacterial decomposition of wastes); salinity (concentration of inorganic salts, which simultaneously determines the osmotic pressure and nutritional potential of the habitat); and pH (acidity or alkalinity). Extremes in abiotic conditions exclude all but adapted species. The salinity of marine waters excludes about three-fifths of known protozoan species and simple populations occur in such specialized habitats as arctic waters, hot springs, acid bogs and anaerobic sites, (deep mud and the gut, for example). Protozoa in anaerobic habitats are killed by atmospheric oxygen, and are known as 'obligate anaerobes'.

Rumen ciliates are adapted to function anaerobically in alkaline conditions. If the host is fed pelleted food the rumen becomes acid and the ciliate population declines. The young ruminant receives ciliates from the mother's cud, when she licks her offspring. While the young is suckling, the rumen is acid, but as weaning proceeds, the rumen gradually becomes alkaline, and the ciliates are established. Birds can be infected with a sporozoan causing avian malaria. Malaria-causing species live in reticulo-endothelial or liver cells, occasionally passing into the blood, where rapid population increases occur due to multiple fission in red blood cells, subsequent lysis releasing the offspring to infect other red corpuscles. In birds, the blood population fluctuates diurnally, coincident with similar fluctuations in the hosts' temperature and metabolic activity. Among free-living protozoa autotrophs are the most directly affected by abiotic variations. Fluctuations in light intensity cause variations in activity and density of surface populations of some photosynthetic flagellates, reduced light intensity causing dispersal of the population, which is replaced by other planktonic protozoa. Hence diurnal variations are seen in planktonic protozoan populations in small pools.

Abiotic variations affect all protozoa at the cellular level, altering permeability, the activity of synthetic, digestive and reproductive enzymes, and motility, but they also modify the chemical structure of dissolved food, species composition and activity in microflora, and nutrition and activity of parasites' hosts. Fauré-Fremiet (1967) pointed out that tolerance ranges of heterotrophic protozoa are equivalent to those of their natural, food-supplying associates. Thus it is difficult to separate direct (cellular) and indirect (nutritional) effects of abiotic variations on heterotrophs. Seasonal variations have been observed in many heterotrophic populations, but these may not be directly due to temperature variations, since the latter, combined with seasonal turnover in natural waters, have direct effects on food organisms. The complexity of this problem is indicated by the list of thirty abiotic and biological factors which Braarud (1962) suggested may be significant in determining initiation and maintenance of protozoan blooms in oceans.

Protozoan Responses to Adverse Conditions

Abiotic changes beyond the species' tolerance ranges induce protective responses. Many protozoa encyst – the cell becomes dormant and secretes a protective coat – excystation being induced by improvement in environmental conditions. Cysts can be carried to a new site by winds, water, insects, animals, or birds. Parasites of the mouth and the urogenital system are transferred by contact, gut parasites passing out in faeces, infecting a new host when it ingests contaminated food. Protozoa parasitizing vertebrate blood and cells are 'inoculated' into a new host by insect vectors – biting or blood-sucking species in attendance on the host.

Rapid cystation is characteristic of protozoa native to habitats subject to rapid changes and desiccation, notably soil and sand, the rate of change in abiotic conditions being proportional to the volume of fluid. Flexible cystation and excystation reactions combined with rapid population increase explain the appearance and disappearance of protozoan populations as environmental conditions change. A sessile ciliate, *Vorticella octava* (Figure 3), forms cysts which are activated by increased osmotic stress, thus in laboratory cultures excystation is induced by washing the cysts with distilled water. The author has maintained this species in culture, feeding the vorticellas with bacteria, originally isolated from the natural habitat. Vorticella populations reached 7,000 per millilitre of culture medium. On achieving limiting density the entire population encysted within 24 hours. If the cysts were

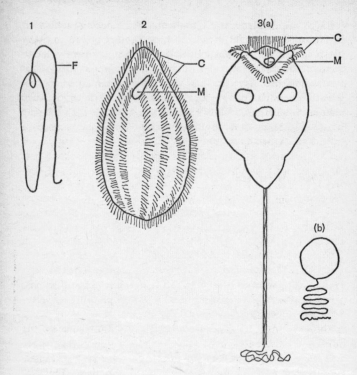

Figure 1. *Euglena gracilis*; a green, autotrophic flagellate.

Figure 2. *Tetrahymena pyriformis*; a phagotrophic (vegetarian) ciliate; a swimming ciliate, with rows of cilia.

Figure 3. *Vorticella octava* (a) adult, (b) cyst; a sessile ciliate with a contractile stalk (the spiral thread in the stalk is the contractile element). Three food-vacuoles are shown in the body. Protozoa have no discrele digestive system. Food is 'pinched off' into vacuoles, in which digestion occurs. Indigestible material is ejected from the body at a point near the mouth in ciliates.
The cyst remains attached to the contracted stalk in this species.

Abbreviations: C – cilia
F – flagellum
M – mouth

washed with distilled water, then a culture of bacteria added to feed the emerging vorticellas, the entire feeding population was re-established within 90 minutes. The vorticellas were isolated from a sewage treatment plant, and other populations have since been established from samples of stagnant pond water. This species is a voracious vegetarian, requiring dense and active bacterial populations to satisfy demands. Excystation in response to osmotic stress ensures emergence when the habitat is diluted, such dilution inevitably being accompanied by washing in of organic nutrients which stimulate bacterial activity. Thus the vorticellas are active in the optimal period of bacterial activity, the same environmental stimuli inducing vorticellid emergence, and the bloom in the food organisms.

Population Diversity in Relation to Combined Influences from Nutritional and Abiotic Conditions; Polluted and Fertile Habitats

Free-living protozoan populations are frequently more diverse than the active population seen when a fresh sample is examined, since many species occur as cysts. If a sample of soil or pond water is examined, then diluted with a nutrient medium such as hay infusion or bacteriological peptones, population diversity increases, since the microflora, stimulated by the added nutrients, enriches the medium with dissolved food and prey. This enrichment stimulates excystation, and successions of dominant protozoa occur, reflecting changing chemical and biological conditions. First osmotrophic flagellates and amoebae dominate; then, as microflora and protozoa increase, phagotrophs become dominant – vegetarians followed by carnivores – successions culminating in dominance of sessile ciliates with strong feeding currents, which can trap the microflora and dissolved food remaining after previous microbial activity has almost exhausted the added nutrients.

These successions follow pollution of natural waters with organic wastes. The 'saprobic system' classifies the dominant protozoa according to the gross degree of organic pollution they prefer. Protozoan population structure varies with distance from the source of pollution, or, in the case of occasional pollution of standing waters, the protozoan community varies with time, both spatial and temporal variations indicating progress of microbial degradation of the wastes. Information on the biochemistry and nutrition of most of the species involved in successions induced by pollution is fragmentary, due to difficulties in maintaining such species under controlled laboratory conditions, so precise correlation of population structure, and chemical and biological conditions in the environment are impossible.

Highly specialized versions of these interspecies population fluctuations occur in 'activated sludge' waste disposal plants, where sewage and trade wastes are passed through a series of aeration tanks. The dominant protozoa are ciliates dependent on the microflora selected by the type of wastes treated. The microflora is largely bacterial, part of the population being flocculated together, the flocs supporting the ciliates – creeping or sessile species. The micro-population is the activated sludge, and settles out when the purified wastes plus activated sludge are run into settlement tanks. The supernatant is sufficiently pure for discharge into adjacent natural waters. Part of the settled sludge is re-circulated to feed on incoming wastes, and the excess, which develops as the micro-organisms feed on the wastes, is used as fertilizer, or dumped at sea, where it fertilizes fisheries. The success of the native sludge ciliates is due to their habit (which permits retention in sludge during settlement and re-circulation, swimming species being swept out), and their nutritional preferences – sessile ciliates feeding on the dense, specialized microflora and its products, creeping species browsing on floc surfaces and free microflora, or being predatory on other native protozoa. Recurrent fluctuations occur in sessile, vegetarian creeping, and carnivorous species, indicating variations in quantity and quality of wastes treated, and the response of the microflora to these variations. If flagellates or amoebae become dominant, the plant is functioning abnormally. These protozoa partake in the natural type of succession when the plant is started up, after 'seeding' with sludge from an active plant, the flagellate/amoebae/ciliate successions indicating the establishment of the microflora efficient in purification; subsequent maintenance of this population is dependent on a continuous flow of the type of wastes which initiated its development. Drastic alteration in the nature of the wastes treated, or plant malfunction, such as break-down in aeration, causes disruption of the approximately steady state condition, with resultant reversion to inefficient microflora, indicated by dominance of flagellates and amoebae. The protozoa in plants treating large amounts of trade wastes are adapted to resist toxic factors, and feed on the microflora adapted to degrade such wastes. High concentrations of metals or phenols, for example, are toxic to natural populations if discharged occasionally into rivers or lakes. In plants habitually receiving such wastes the microflora and protozoa flourish. In natural waters, sudden mortality of the micro-population acts as an index of discharge of toxic wastes which may not be detectable by other methods, since micro-organisms are sensitive to very dilute quantities of toxic wastes.

Discharge of untreated sewage, or of wastes which have been treated for short periods, thus still containing considerable undegraded organic matter, often initiates huge flagellate blooms. Similarly, storms and seasonal turnover in standing waters have been observed to coincide with, or precede flagellate blooms. Laboratory studies on flagellates in pure culture show that vitamin B_{12} is an essential requirement for many bloom-formers. The vitamin is synthesized by soil and water microflora, accumulating in soil and silts, in activated sludge, and in water fertilized by organic pollution, which stimulates activity in local microflora. Thus flagellate blooms may be triggered by increase in B_{12} content of the habitat, then maintained by the greatly increased concentrations of dissolved food, notably organic phosphate and nitrogen – also shown by laboratory studies to be growth stimulants – providing other conditions are favourable. The most dramatic blooms are those causing 'red-water' in offshore waters all over the world, these blooms of red-pigmented, vitamin B_{12}-requiring, protozoa frequently causing great mortality in fish populations. But increased organic B_{12} concentrations are favourable when diluted in open seas, hence the fertility of fisheries over mud-banks, and the stimulation of planktonic populations by dumping of sewage plant products, which thus ultimately return to land as food, since the plankton supports shoals of fish.

Protozoa and Fertility of Soil and Water

Some aspects of the role of protozoa in maintaining the fertility of their environment have been indicated in the preceding discussion of various populations. They form a living net, trapping dissolved food and minute prey, making them available to larger multicellular organisms predatory on protozoa, and by-products of protozoan activity are available to associated micro-organisms, thus maintaining nutrient turnover. The relation between environmental fertility and protozoan activity has been well studied for soil and sea.

Soil Fertility

In light, fertile soil there are flourishing protozoan communities associated with the 'rhizosphere' – the area around plant roots. The rhizosphere harbours rich microflora, nourished in part by root secretions, the microbial community, in turn, enriching soil with their metabolic by-products. Biczók (1963) studied some protozoan rhizosphere populations and recorded 63 flagellate species, 98 amoeba species and 97 ciliate species, which appeared to be selected by the microflora and animal prey rather than by the physical characteristics of the habitat. He grouped the protozoa according to diet thus: 40 per cent bacteria; 15 per cent bacteria and algae; 15 per cent other protozoa; 10 per cent bacteria and detritus; 6 per cent bacteria and flagellates; 3 per cent bacteria, algae, and flagellates; 2 per cent bacteria and fungi; 2 per cent algae, and small protozoa; 3 per cent other (unspecified) food. The ciliate species in the rhizosphere also occur in other hibitats; 30 per cent associated with humus and plants; 18 per cent in soil; 1 per cent with rotting matter; 6 per cent in fresh water; 3 per cent other sources. He found that the quantity and quality of protozoa in rhizospheres in a single meadow varied according to the plants, different species associating with different plants, and population density and composition varied with root depth. When plants were cut down, and in fields of stubble, protozoan populations were sparse.

In laboratory experiments, where plants were grown in soil covered with foil to prevent growth of algae and mosses, Darbyshire and Greaves (1967) found much simpler populations (only flagellates and amoebae occurring in significant numbers), and found less difference between populations in planted and unplanted soil. These differences were probably due to the very restricted microflora (entirely bacterial) selected by laboratory conditions, exclusion of light preventing growth of photosynthetic species in microflora and protozoan communities. The restricted food supply, compared with the natural microflora recorded by Biczók, markedly restricted diversity in the protozoan fauna.

Fertility of the Sea

Photosynthetic flagellates, in company with photosynthetic microflora, form the 'grass' of the open sea, fertilizing the waters with their metabolic by-products, and feeding other micro-organisms, and crustacean and fish larvae. The composition and density of planktonic protozoan populations varies geographically, with temperature, ocean depth, currents and predator populations, these and many other factors being discussed by Wood (1967).

Planktonic amoebae, and certain flagellate species have shells or skeletons incorporating nutritionally valuable minerals, for example calcium and silica. These predatory protozoa are thus important food for crustacean larvae in the plankton, and also concentrate these minerals from surface waters, whence they sink when the protozoa die, contributing to vertical transport of nutrients. The minerals are cemented together with organic secretions in many species, hence organic nutrients are also carried to deeper waters.

Only one group of ciliates – the tintinnids – are significant in planktonic populations of open seas. These predatory ciliates browse at the fringes of plankton blooms, and their protective vase-like shells of debris, cemented with organic matter, contribute to concentration of particulate food in surface waters. In most oceans, tintinnid populations are small, but Gold (1968) studied laboratory populations, and concluded that these voracious predators are potentially capable of decimating other planktonic populations.

Interactions between Members of Microflora/Protozoan Communities

Abiotic and nutritional parameters define protozoan environments and control protozoan populations, but population fluctuations and species distribution are also significantly modified by complex interactions between protozoa and their associates – prey or host, gut and mouth parasites being subject to influences from both microflora and host. Lucas (1955) defined protozoan inter-actions as 'predatory' and 'non-predatory'. The latter involve reactions to chemical factors produced by associates, which may stimulate or repress activity.

Protozoa Predatory-Prey Relationships; Carnivorous and Vegetarian

The relationships obtaining in higher taxa also operate in protozoan populations – prey increases stimulating predatory activity; maintenance of prey populations depending on continuing food supply and ability to escape or hide. However, protozoan predators are also affected by chemical stimuli, detecting large prey if it is injured, leaking body contents apparently being the attractant for swarms of predators, smaller prey attracting predators by virtue of by-products of metabolic activity.

The predatory ciliate *Tetrahymena vorax* can exist in small-mouthed (microstome) or large-mouthed (macrostome) form, the microstome-macrostome transformation being induced by proximity of prey. Buhse (1967) studied this transformation in pure cultures of the ciliates. In chemically defined medium, where the ciliates obtain all food from solution tetrahymenas were in microstome form. If a culture of prey (another *Tetrahymena* species) was placed in contact with the predators, but mixing prevented by separating the two populations with a membrane permitting only chemical diffusion, the microstome-macrostome change occurred in 70–90 per cent of the predators within 7 hours. The factor stimulating the change could be chemically extracted from actively growing prey cultures, and was found to be a low molecular weight compound released by the prey.

Morphological changes are also induced in certain rumen ciliates, according to the host's condition. These species store products of fodder digestion as skeletal plates of complex polysaccharides, digesting the plates when the host's feeding rate does not satisfy ciliate demand. By-products of ciliate metabolism are utilized by rumen microflora, thus stimulating fodder digestion. Hungate (1966) calculated that the host receives one-fifth of its requirements from ciliate fermentation activity, and from protein obtained when ciliates are themselves digested on passing to the intestine.

Predation stimulates activity in microflora, since it is prevented from reaching limiting density, and thus remains active as long as food is available. Potentially, microflora populations control protozoa in two ways; by supplying food and by production of antagonistic factors – some species contain toxic pigment; others secrete antibiotics inhibiting or preventing protozoan reproduction; others secrete digestive enzymes which destroy some protozoan cells; and acid or alkaline by-products may alter environmental pH, repressing activity in certain protozoa and some species in the microflora. Thus the dominant species in the microflora, maintained by the dominant vegetarian protozoa, creates nutritional and chemical conditions which stimulate some protozoa and repress others. Changes in abiotic conditions stimulate other species in the microflora, these new dominants creating a new range of environmental conditions. Thus various permutations of species in the microflora support different groups of species in the protozoan community – osmotrophs, vegetarians and carnivores. The dominant complex of protozoa is thus stimulated by nutritional conditions created by the interaction between environmental conditions and microflora, and is resistant to any antagonistic conditions created by dominant species in the microflora, which suppress activity in other microorganisms.

Stimulation and Repression by Protozoan Interactions

Protozoa also interact chemically. Jensen and Meyers (1967) showed that the amoeba *Acanthamoeba castellani* secretes factors repressing excystation in related amoebae – an effective method of suppressing potential competitors. Stillwell (1967) cultured two unrelated ciliates separately in pure culture. One species, *Colpidium campylum*, released a high molecular weight compound which accumulated during the phase of active growth, then disappeared as the population reached limiting density, presumably due to utilization when the medium no longer supplied sufficient food. The factor was isolated chemically, and added to freshly inoculated *Tetrahymena* cultures. A 50–60 per cent increase in population resulted, but no growth stimulation occurred if the factor was added to actively growing populations. Stillwell postulated that the factor does not act as a nutrient *per se*, but stimulates phagotrophy (feeding activity), thus increasing intake of essential small molecules, during the critical 'lag-phase' when freshly inoculated organisms adjust to new culture medium. Other phagotrophic protozoa in pure culture are stimulated by addition of non-nutrient particles such as activated charcoal or polystyrene globes. In pure culture the protozoa must obtain all food from solution, in contrast to the concentrated food obtained in nature by digesting solids. Inert particles probably stimulate growth by adsorbing, hence concentrating, dissolved food, which the protozoa take in phagotrophically.

Release of subsequently utilized by-products has been observed in many pure culture studies, and may be significant in nature, maintaining blooms when the initial food supply is exhausted. High molecular weight compounds may also act as adsorbants for other species, which would compete for the by-products. The relevance of by-products in nature is a subject of controversy, some workers arguing that they are diluted in nature, and their effects are thus not as significant as culture studies indicate. However, in small habitats, and where populations are very dense, their effects could be very important.

Parasite-Host Interactions

The pathogenicity of protozoan parasites is an index of the evolutionary state of the host-parasite relationship. Ideally, it should be mutually beneficial to ensure survival of both members. Some species of the genera causing malaria and sleeping sickness cause only minor host discomfort, others serious disease. Presumably the most pathogenic species are in early stages of evolutionary adjustment. Parasites must resist the host's defences and take sufficient food without causing host starvation. The success of the population is determined by the host's health. Host malnutrition favours invasion, since production of antibodies is reduced. Invasive phases of otherwise harmless parasites appear to be favoured by host malnutrition, possibly because the host's diet does not satisfy protozoan demand. Hence the parasites attack cells in their search for food, and changes in chemical conditions in the gut may also directly affect protozoan metabolism. Conversely, parasites can exacerbate host malnutrition. Populations of the common, remora-like flagellate, *Giardia intestinalis*, can blanket the lining of the gut, and cause malnutrition in children in under-developed countries.

The rapid reproductive rate of parasites favours emergence of mutants permitting constant adjustment to their environment, notably rapid development of drug-resistance; hence the never-ending search for anti-malarial drugs.

Future Directions in Studies on Protozoan Populations

Until recently, ecological and experimental techniques were inadequate for accurate definition of environmental determinants and details of protozoan biochemistry and physiology. The complexity of most protozoan environments and diets offers great challenges in reproducing the species' required conditions in controlled laboratory cultures, namely using media of known chemical composition in the absence of natural associates (in 'defined, axenic' media). Only a handful of species are available in pure culture, others requiring media containing plant or animal tissues, many also needing at least one associate, or, at best, killed suspensions or extracts of food organisms. There is a similar gap in information on many protozoan associates; thus, although protozoa can be seen ingesting microflora and fluid, the species ingested, their cellular composition, and their chemical effect on the environment, are often unknown. Future studies on microflora will accelerate interpretation of fluctuations in free-living protozoan populations.

Our environment is dangerously polluted and overpopulated. Uncontrolled use of chemicals to promote soil fertility and combat disease have caused serious ecological disruptions. Efficient food production and pollution control demand knowledge of the activities of the primary and secondary producers which determine the success of all other animal populations.

Bibliography

REFERENCES CITED

References marked with an asterisk are recommended to the general reader.

Biczók, F., 'Protozoa in the Rhizosphere', in *Progress in Protozoology*. 2nd Int. Conf. Protozool., London, 1965. Excerpta Medica Foundation, Amsterdam, p. 120 (Abstr.).

Braarud, T., Species distribution in marine phytoplankton. J. Oceanog. Soc. Japan. *20*, 628–49, 1962.

Buhse, H. E., 'Microstome-macrostome Transformation in *Tetrahymena vorax* Strain V_2 Type S Induced by a Transforming Principle, Stomatin', *J. Protozool.* 14 (4), 608–18, 1967.

Darbyshire, J. F., and Greaves, M. P., 'Protozoa and Bacteria in the Phizosphere of *Synapis alba L., Trifolium repens L.* and *Lolium perenne L.*', *Can. J. Microbiol,* 1967. 13, 1057–68.

*Fauré-Fremiet E., 'Chemical aspects of ecology', in *Chemical Zoology,* ed. Marcel Florkin and Bradley T. Scheer. Vol. I, Protozoa, ed. George W. Kidder, pp. 21–54, Academic Press, New York, 1967.

Gold, K., 'The Role of Ciliates in Marine Ecology. II. Feeding characteristics of *Tintinnopsis* sp. *in vitro.*', *J. Protozool.* 14 (Suppl.), Abstract no. 47, 1967.

Hungate, R. E., *The Rumen and its Microbes,* Academic Press, New York and London, 1966.

Jensen, T., and Meyers, D., *Characterization of an Inhibitor Produced by Acanthamoeba castellani,* in *J. Protozool.* 14 (Suppl.), Abstract no. 14, 1967.

Lucas, C. E., *Papers in Marine Biology and Oceanography,* pp. 139–48, Pergamon Press, Oxford, 1955.

Stillwell, R. H., '*Colpidium* produced RNA as a growth stimulant for *Tetrahymena*', *J. Protozool.* 14 (I), 19–22, 1967.

*Wood, E. J. F., *Microbiology of Oceans and Estuaries,* Elsevier Publishing Company, London and New York, 1967.

FURTHER READING

Hawkes, H. A., *The Ecology of Waste Treatment,* Pergamon Press, 1963. (Very readable discussion of the microbiological aspects of pollution and waste treatment.)

Jahn, T. L., and Jahn, F. F., *How to Know the Protozoa,* Wm. C. Brown, Dubuque, 1949. (Excellent small book for recognition of species.)

Kudo, F. R., *Protozoology,* 5th edition, Charles C. Thomas, Springfield, Illinois, 1966. (Recommended for details of taxonomy and ecology; lavishly illustrated.)

Manwell, R. D., *Introduction to Protozoology,* St Martins Press, New York, 1961. (A very readable outline of a complicated subject.)

Noland, L. E., and Gojdics, M., 'Ecology of Free-living Protozoa', in *Research in Protozoology.* Vol. 2., ed. Tze Tuan Chen, Pergamon Press, 1967. (This review, like the recommended references, is technical but readable, summarizing present knowledge on protozoan population dynamics.)

The Population Biology of Plants

John L. Harper

All living organisms are potentially capable of increasing their numbers by a geometric progression from generation to generation. This potential is realized when a crop is sown and sufficient seed harvested to allow both the next generation's crop to be harvested and the excess to be taken for human or animal consumption. It is shown by the expansion of weed populations in a garden, the multiplication of strawberries by runners and even by the multiplication of single individuals: a particularly striking example of this is the King Edward potato, of which all specimens are believed to be the vegetative parts of a single initial plant. However the most spectacular demonstrations of population growth in plants are found when species successfully establish themselves in a new area. *Salvinia auriculata*, a water fern, was sent to Colombo, Ceylon for study in 1939. In 1942 it was observed in quantity in rice paddy fields and by 1955 had put 25,000 acres of rice paddy out of cultivation. Another famous example of multiplication is that of *Elodea canadensis*, the Canadian pond weed, which was first detected in Britain in 1847; by 1849 it was already very abundant in Derbyshire and Staffordshire and by 1852 was present in such vast quantities that it was filling water courses and hindering barge traffic.

The growth of population is particularly startling in aquatic plants, and the water hyacinth *Eichhornia crassipes* may multiply at such a rate in the Congo that it has been observed passing Leopoldville at the rate of 150 tons an hour (despite the expenditure of 50,000,000 francs a year in attempts to keep the river clear). In laboratory cultures even the common duck weed (*Lemna minor*) may double its number of fronds every two and a half days. If this rate of multiplication is continued a square inch of Lemna plants will come to occupy an acre in about 55 days.

Many of the most catastrophic increases in plant populations have occurred in species which have become weeds of agricultural land. These were often introduced as apparently harmless garden specimens and escaped to colonize enormous acreages of land; prickly pears were introduced to Australia in this way late in the nineteenth century and by 1900 had colonized 10,000,000 acres; by 1925 not only were 60,000,000 acres of land densely covered by this cactus but half of this area was so densely colonized as to be impenetrable by man and large animals.

In practice, explosive increases in plant populations tend to be followed either by a period of stability or of decline; all three phases can sometimes be observed when Canadian pondweed is introduced to a new artificial pond. Although the processes of invasion of new territories by weedy species provide the most spectacular examples of plants realizing their potential for increase, the process of natural succession in vegetation itself involves successive phases of population growth by one species of plant after another until some form of relatively stable state is reached.

The role of the population biologist is to study the numbers of organisms and to attempt to explain the rates of change in number, or the cause of stability. In ecological studies there is some division of labour between the population biologist concerned with numbers and the production biologist concerned with factors affecting mass, energy flow and productivity. In practice, however, the study of populations and the study of productivity do not have neat boundaries.

Much of the study of the population biology of plants has been made using very simple communities composed of one or at most two species. In this type of study (which originated very largely in studies of crop systems) attempts have been made to follow what happens to populations of plants which are sown in pure stands at different densities. The effect of density can then be followed in terms of the numbers of plants that survive, the size they achieve and the number of seeds that the adult population

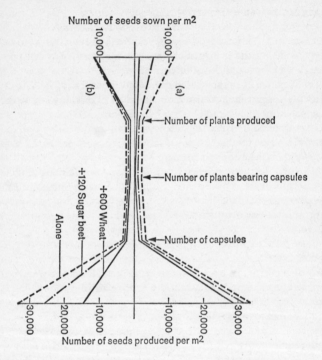

Number of seeds sown per m²

10,000   10,000

(b)   (a)

←—Number of plants produced

←—Number of plants bearing capsules

Alone   +120 Sugar beet   +600 Wheat

←—Number of capsules

30,000 20,000 10,000   10,000 20,000 30,000

Number of seeds produced per m²

Figure 1. Stages in the production of seed by populations of corn cockle (*Agrostemma githago*). To the right of the vertical line is shown the consequences of sowing three widely different densities of seed. The seed produced by these populations was closely similar. To the left of the vertical line is shown the effects of sowing corn cockle at one density alone, and in the presence of 600 wheat grains or 120 sugar beet seeds per m². These associated species have a profound effect on seed production. Reprinted from Harper and Gajic, 1961.

in turn produces (Figure 1). Further complexity may be introduced into such experimental systems by the addition of a second species, and variations can be played in the experimental systems by changing the densities of the two species, their proportions and their relative times of growth as well as the patterns of arrangement of the species in the mixed population. This experimental approach constitutes what may be called a synthetic approach to the population biology of plants. The synthetic approach has revealed that plants respond to population density both by a plastic response in size and reproductive capacity and by a mortality rate which increases with increasing population density. There is evidence from this sort of experimental study that the response to the density of neighbouring plants is a specific response – the fate of two species in mixture being determined by the way each responds to the density of the other (Harper, 1967).

In contrast to the 'synthetic' approach there is an approach best described as 'analytic' in which the density of populations of plants may be altered experimentally, or other changes in the environment made and alterations in the dynamics of the population then followed. A particularly intriguing form of this experimentation involves the deliberate removal of one species from a natural mixed community and observations on the changes that the other species may show. This type of experimentation has been made much easier by the discoveries of modern very selective herbicides which can be used as a most elegant ecological tool for the selective manipulation of plant numbers in mixed populations in the wild or in agricultural systems.

The Stages in the Determination of Plant Density

The density of a particular species in an area of natural or artificial vegetation may be determined at a given time simply by the supply of available seed. There are species in the British flora of which the numbers in any given year seem to be determined simply by the numbers of seeds of the species that have appeared by accidental introduction into Britain. This is true of those species which

never manage to set viable seeds in the British climate and whose
numbers are therefore dependent on the recruitment of new seed
every year from overseas. Many such alien species arrive in
Britain every year in wool, or as contaminants in packing materials
on goods imported from overseas. These species appear spas-
modically in the main wool manufacturing regions of Britain
particularly in the neighbourhood of the Tweed and around
ports, particularly Southampton. The shortage of seed is also
likely to determine the number of plants of a given species that
are present at early stages in a plant succession until the species
has multiplied to a population sufficiently large that the seed
supply is no longer the limit on population size.

The numbers of a particular species of plant may be limited by
a shortage of sites suitable for germination and seedling establishment. The establishment of plants from seed in nature is a very
chancy matter. In agricultural or forestry practice the depth of
sowing and the density are under careful control but in nature
each seed produced is at risk and its chance of landing in sites
suitable for germination is a variable risk depending on the state
of the soil, the activities of seed eaters like birds, of seed buriers
like earthworms, and of seed decomposers. It is salutory to
visualize how heterogeneous a soil surface is as a landing ground
for a unit of the size of a seed; landing sites suitable for germination may be very infrequent. On a carefully managed lawn the
only suitable sites for daisy germination may be worm casts and
the frequency of daisy clumps can often be attributed directly
to the frequency of worm casts. Differences in the frequency of
suitable germination sites can therefore account for considerable
differences in seedling density even when the rate of seed fall is
constant. Cameron (1935) in a study of ragwort (*Senecio jacobaea*)
sowed 100 seeds per square foot in natural habitats of short turf,
overgrazed pasture and open soil. The number of seedlings obtained was equivalent too, 86,000 and 2,300,000 per acre respectively! It is easy to underestimate the highly specialized and
often species – specific requirements for successful germination.
The acorn must find itself at least half buried if it is to avoid desiccation and germinate successfully. Some seeds require light for

germination, including those of many species which bear very small seeds; some, like the poppies, require rather precise conditions of alternating temperature between day and night for their successful germination. The depth of the seed in the soil may be critical in determining whether it receives the right light intensity and the right alternating temperature for its germination, whether it avoids desiccation from being too near the surface and yet is not too deep in the soil for the cotyledons or first leaves to be raised quickly above the soil surface.

The size of a seedling population will be determined by the product of (a) the availability of seeds, and (b) the availability of micro-sites suitable for germination (the concept of 'micro-site' is useful in this context for naming the zone not much bigger than the seed and of which the environment determines whether the seed germinates or not). As a result of this interplay between the frequency of seeds and the frequency of safe micro-sites, seedlings may develop as a few isolated very scattered individuals too far apart to interfere with each other significantly or at 'mustard and cress' densities in which individual seedlings start to affect each other's growth a few days after germination. The denser the population the earlier in the life cycle do seedlings interfere with each other's activities, and the density of neighbours whether of the same or of different species may have the effect of hastening death or modifying the growth rate. There are of course, many risks to which a young seedling is subject even when the population is so sparse that individuals are not affecting each other at all. Many of these risks are unsuspected until an attempt is made to follow the detailed day to day history of a seedling population. Hazards such as being knocked over by a rain-drop may be very real for a seedling as delicate as, for example, that of a poppy. The humid micro-environment in the upper layers of the soil is favourable for several fungi which cause seedling death, most notably species of *Pythium*. Young seedlings are often found lining earth worm burrows and may form the diet of slugs and snails. Many of the causes of death of young seedlings are still quite obscure and it is a very difficult task for the population biologist to ascribe causes of death even when a seedling population is followed from day to day; seedlings may be quite literally here today and gone tomorrow, without trace.

Where seedlings develop at such a density that they modify one another's environment the mortality risk to each individual may be increased. A dense stand of seedlings itself produces conditions of high humidity which favour pathogenic attack. This is a well known phenomenon in forestry nurseries and in the growth of mustard and cress. Where seedlings are clumped densely together, predators may take a higher proportion of the population than they do if the individuals occur more regularly or sparsely; for example wire worm populations tend to migrate along the rows of a cereal crop moving from one seedling to its nearest neighbour rather than across the rows. Such density-induced mortality has the effect of thinning denser populations to a greater extent than sparse ones and so of bringing adult populations within a narrower range of densities than the starting seedling populations.

The density of seedlings also affects their individual growth rate. Neighbours may be making demands on similar resources of the environment at the same time. In the case of plants these resources are almost inevitably light, water and nutrients and perhaps carbon dioxide. The proximity of neighbours, where it is sufficient to reduce the amount of light falling on each seedling, may cause etiolation and will certainly restrict growth rate. The restricted growth rate in turn results in the development of a restricted root system, tapping smaller volumes of soil making the plant more sensitive to water shortage and nutrient shortage than one that is uninhibited (Milthorpe, 1961). As a plant population under density stress becomes resource limited, so the rate of growth of the population (in mass – not numbers) becomes determined more by the availability of the limiting environmental resource than by the number of individual plants: the rate of growth of the individual then reflects the division of limited resources among the number of individuals present. As a result the dry matter production of populations which vary greatly in density may be the same per unit area of land. Individuals in the population of highest density interfere with each other first, and with the passage of time successively lower and lower densities become limited by environmental resources. This leads to the law of constant final yield in which production of dry matter per unit area eventually becomes independent of the population density. Sometimes at very high densities there may even be a decline in production because the plants produced are so long and spindly that they collapse. In practice it is often impossible to study the growth of plants in population at very high density because the density is reduced by mortality.

This picture of two density-dependent processes, mortality and plasticity, operating in a population of a single species of plant is, of course, grossly simplified. One common simplification involves considering average behaviour and this obscures interesting aspects of individual behaviour. The stress of density is not absorbed equally by all the members of a plant population even when it is a uniformly spaced stand of a single species. Populations under the stress of density develop a hierarchy in which those individuals which germinated first quickly gain an advantage over later developing neighbours; placing their cotyledons and leaves higher quicker, or their roots further faster, than the later emerging amongst their neighbours; the advantage so gained becomes cumulative. The consequence of this exaggeration of inequality in the members of the population is that a group of seedlings which starts off with a normally distributed weight frequency become progressively skewed towards a log-normal frequency distribution in which the population has a few large individuals and very many small ones. Even in genetically very homogeneous plant populations small differences in germination time appear to be responsible for the division of the population into a continuum of have's and have not's; thus it is misleading to think of a population which develops under density stress absorbing this stress by a modification and reduction in size of the average plant. Much of the density stress is absorbed by the suppression of a variable part of the population. This suppressed part of the population appears to be the part most liable to die, and the process of density-induced thinning is therefore interlinked with the process of density-induced plasticity. Moreover density-induced thinning continues in some species at least through to plant maturity and is not a purely seedling phenomenon. Figure 2 reproduces the results of the work of Yoda *et al.*, Japanese workers who studied a population of *Erigeron canadensis* in an old field. This very dense population was observed at an early seedling stage when the density was of the order of 100,000 seedlings per square metre. Yoda and his colleagues applied five levels of fertilizer treatment to this field, 1, 2, 3, 4, and 5, representing decreasing levels of fertility. In Figure 2 the changes in both population size, numbers of plants per unit area, and mean plant weight are shown at successive times. It is clear from these data that the process of thinning and the process of change in plant weight are very regularly related in the experiment and the process of thinning occurred right through the growing season of the population. Conditions of high fertility favoured more rapid plant growth *and* more rapid mortality. It is an interesting aspect of this type of population regulation that the most fertile conditions are associated with the greatest risk to individual survival.

Recently both botanists and zoologists have begun to use the concept of 'the strategy of a life cycle' in a search for ways of quantifying those aspects of the natural history of organisms which are major determinants of population behaviour. The logarithmic curve of population growth is a relatively crude but very useful theoretical base on which to build population models:

$$\frac{dN}{dt} = rN\frac{K-N}{K}$$

In this equation the rate of growth of the population N (usually in numbers, though the model is applicable to mass) is considered as determined by an intrinsic rate of unimpeded exponential growth r observed when individuals are not interfering with each other's activities. K represents an upper limit of population size determined by some restriction that growth of the population itself brings. In an unstable habitat, populations will spend much of their time in recovery from the most recent catastrophe. Species favoured in these circumstances will be likely to be those

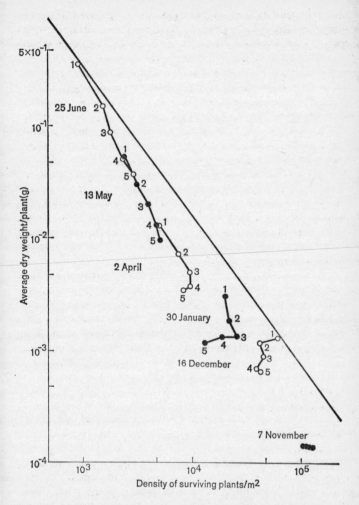

Figure 2. The changes in numbers and weight of a field population of *Erigeron canadensis* in a single season. The field contained a steep fertility gradient, exaggerated by graded fertilizer application. The plot numbers 1–5 represent the order of *decreasing* fertility. Redrawn from Yoda *et al.*, 1963.

with high r values. In contrast, populations of stable habitats are likely to spend more of their time living at the limits of their resources – that is, dominated in their behaviour by their reaction to neighbours and to K.

r-dominated species are, for example, the weeds of arable land and gardens, the pioneer species of sand dunes, the inhabitants of open glades in woodlands. These plants are successful by virtue of their ability (a) to invade new areas, and (b) to multiply fast after invasion. Their reproductive strategy usually involves a large seed output of readily dispersed (usually small) seeds and precocious reproduction. *Poa annua* (annual meadow grass) and *Senecio vulgaris* (groundsel) are good representatives of this group of plants. Precocious reproduction is a peculiarly effective way of ensuring a rapid rate population growth – a point illustrated by the fact that a population of organisms which produce two off-spring in the first year and then die, will increase as fast as a population of organisms each of which produces one offspring a year and lives for ever.

However, species with precocious reproduction and a large number of seeds, seldom use the whole reproductive output for immediate population expansion, and it is characteristic of weedy species that a proportion of the seed remains dormant for several years. The proportion of seeds which germinate quickly and the fraction allocated by the species to remain dormant presum-ably represents a compromise between (a) the importance of precocious reproduction to maintain rapid population growth, and (b) the importance of ensuring that some seed will survive a catastrophe which kills all the growing plants. Attempts have recently been made to analyse, in computer models, the optimal strategy of dormant versus non-dormant seeds in hazardous environments (Cohen, 1968).

Species of plants which spend much of their time under stress incurred by the density of their neighbours (K dominated species) succeed by the ability to pre-empt environmental resources. Limiting consumable resources for a plant are light, water, nutrients and CO_2, and a successful plant in a struggle for exist-ence is one which by growing earlier, or faster than its neighbour, gains a greater share of these resources. Organs which enable a new year's shoot to be expanded quickly (corms, bulbs, tubers, etc.) bring just this advantage over neighbours – particularly over neighbours which establish from small seeds. Organs which ensure that foliage is borne high above neighbours (the arborescent habit) bring similar advantages.

It seems reasonable to suppose that plants have limited energy resources at their disposal and that allocation of these to organs of perennation, or long stems and petioles, leaves less for allocation to reproductive ends. The different life cycles and forms of plants can there be usefully considered as strategic compromises between systems maximizing r and systems adapted to succeed in a struggle for existence with neighbours.

It is particularly interesting that many perennial plants possess two distinct means of reproduction – by seed and by vegetative means. Such plants – for example Coltsfoot *Tussilago farfara* or the strawberry – possess two different r values. Seed reproduction, involving a high r value, is important in invading new sites and involves very high expenditure on hostages to fortune. Vegetative reproduction, usually giving a much lower r value, is ineffective in colonizing new areas, but is a powerful means of exploiting a localized zone after initial colonization. When vegetatively produced offspring remain in physical union with the parent, the risks in establishment are minimal and vegetative propagules normally represent a much higher capital investment of resources per individual than investment in a seed. Again the comparison of the reproductive strategy of species in terms of the relative allocation of resources invested in high capital, low risk, and low capital, high risk reproduction enables a quantitative element to be brought into phenomena of natural history.

It has recently been pointed out by Slobodkin and others that life is an existential game in which success is measured by continuing to play the game. A successful reproductive strategy is clearly one which guards against the dangers of losing the game, and so of extinction. The population biology of plants can most easily be appreciated as the record of games played by different strategies against the varied and variable hazards of the environment in which all sorts of plants are playing essentially the same game.

Bibliography

REFERENCES

Cameron, E., *Journal of Ecology*, 23, pp. 265–322, 1935.

Cohen, D., *Journal of Ecology*, 56, pp. 219–28, 1968.

Harper, J. L., and Gajic, D., *Weed Research*, 1, pp. 91–100, 1961.

Milthorpe, F. L., *Symposium of the Society for Experimental Biology*, 15, pp. 330–55, 1961.

Yoda, K., Kira, T., Ogawa, H., and Hozumi, K., *Journal of Biology of Osaka City University*, 14, pp. 107–29, 1963.

FURTHER READING

Harper, J. L., 'Approaches to the study of plant competition', *Symposium of the Society for Experimental Biology*, 15, pp. 1–39, 1961.

Harper, J. L., 'The individual in the population', *Journal of Ecology*, 52 (Supplement), pp. 149–58, 1964.

Harper, J. L., 'A Darwinian approach to plant ecology', *Journal of Ecology*, 55, pp. 247–70, 1967.

Population Growth and Control: Animal Populations

H. G. Andrewartha

Introduction: The Struggle for Existence

Charles Darwin put off writing *The Origin of Species* for more than 20 years after he had convinced himself of the reality of evolution because he could not explain how evolution was caused. Eventually he got his explanation by reading *An Essay on the Principle of Population* by Malthus, published in 1798. Malthus wrote at a time when the population of Europe, responding to scientific discoveries that engendered and arose from the Industrial Revolution of the eighteenth century, was beginning to 'explode'. He wrote of the disastrous starvation and death that he saw to be inevitable as the population increased beyond the capacity of the farms of Europe. Malthus wrote as a prophet of doom. His prophecy was firmly based on the inevitability of population growth and the impossibility of producing enough food for all the people that would be born. In the event his prediction was falsified by the discovery and development of enormous areas of rich farmland in America and Australia but his argument had been soundly based on the facts at his disposal.

Darwin accepted Malthus's argument but, having trained his mind with years of scientific speculation, he saw, with a magnificent flash of imagination, that what Malthus had said in particular about the human population of Europe and their food could be extended to make a general principle that would apply to all species of plants and animals and to all components of their environment, not merely food. The general principle, rather oversimplified, may be stated as follows. If in most generations many more individuals are born than can hope to survive to maturity then it is likely that the survivors will be distinguished by certain qualities which give them a better chance to survive in the environment in which they are struggling to hold a place. If the survivors produce offspring that tend to be like their parents it is likely that the repeated selection of a few survivors from the many that struggle to survive will in time cause noticeable changes in the nature of the animals in the population: they will evolve under the influence of the natural selection which is a consequence of the struggle for existence. With this explanation Darwin was at last ready to begin writing his great book.

Today we can see another important consequence of the struggle for existence and there is satisfaction in the thought that Malthus's essay on population gave Darwin the inspiration that he needed to work out his theory of evolution by natural selection; and Darwin's concept of the struggle for existence contained the germ of another idea that has inspired important modern theories about populations. If a harsh environment causes the premature death (or, what is the same thing, prevents the birth) of many individuals in a population the long-term effect, taken over many generations, may be, as Darwin saw, a change in the nature of the individuals in the population, but the short-term effect may simply be a smaller population in the immediate future. Evolution deals with changes in the nature of the individuals in the population; but population ecology deals with changes in their numbers. In order to explain the numbers of animals in a natural population an ecologist must cast aside (at least for the time being) the long-term evolutionary outcome of the struggle for existence and concentrate his attention instead on the short-term ecological outcome of the struggle.

The Intensity of the Struggle

The African elephant which is one of the least fecund of animals is said to have about 5 offspring during its life and to live for about 50 years. Nevertheless Darwin estimated that if every individual that was born lived out its full term the descendants of one pair would number 19,000,000 after 750 years. At the other extreme it has been calculated for the highly fecund herring that if every individual survived to maturity the descendants of one pair of herrings would be sufficient to fill the North Sea solid with herrings after very few years. Of course animals do not increase like this in nature.

Ecologists calculate a statistic called the 'innate capacity for increase' which measures in a conventional way the capacity for increase characteristic of the species. This statistic is known by the symbol r_m. Convention requires that r_m should be measured (or calculated) for a population that has a 'stable age-distribution'. Age-distribution is important because fecundity and expectation of life vary with age. The stable age-distribution is a useful convention because theoretically it is the particular distribution of age-classes that will remain unchanged from generation to generation in a population that is multiplying uncrowded and free from external restraints. Convention also requires that r_m be measured (or estimated) for a population that is living where temperature, humidity and other components of the 'weather' are optimal and is able to multiply free from any restraint imposed by crowding, shortage of food (or other resource), presence of predators or diseases or indeed any external restraint whatsoever. It is clear from this conventional definition that r_m is the maximum rate of increase attainable by a population having a stable age-distribution. It is not the maximum rate of increase for any population of the species because quite clearly a population made up entirely of the most fecund age group would increase more rapidly than a population with a stable age-distribution which includes some of the less fecund age groups as well.

The statistic r_m belongs to the differential equation for logarithmic population growth:

$$\frac{dN}{dt} = r_m N$$

where t stands for time and N for number in the population, and r_m is the ratio expressing the infinitesimal rate of increase in N per unit time. Given r_m and the duration of a generation one can calculate λ, the finite rate of increase per head per unit time, and R_0 the rate of increase per head per generation. The equation relating the three statistics is:

$$R_0 = e^{r_m T}$$

Both λ and R_0 express ideas which are more realistic and more readily applied to our everyday experience of nature than r_m. E. S. Deevy quotes the following estimates of r_m and R_0 for several well-known animals and I have calculated λ from his figures. These calculations are given in Table 1.

Table 1 Innate Capacity for Increase (r_m), Rate of Increase per Head per Unit Time (λ), and Rate of Increase per Head per Generation (R_0), for Several Animals.

Species	Innate capacity for increase (r_m)	Mean duration of generation	Rate of increase per unit time (λ)	Rate of increase per head per generation (R_0)
Daphnia	0·800 per day	6·8 days	2·23 per day	222
Body louse	0·111 per day	30·9 days	1·13 per day	31
Flour beetle	0·707 per week	7·9 weeks	2·04 per week	275
Rice weevil	0·760 per week	6·2 weeks	2·15 per week	114
Rat	0·103 per week	31·0 weeks	1·11 per week	26
Vole	0·088 per week	20·2 weeks	1·19 per week	6

The statistics λ and R_0 represent highly theoretical ideas because the conventions that define them are most unlikely to be observed in natural populations: the stable age-distribution is hardly likely to occur in natural populations; weather is not likely to be optimal for very long or very often; most species are exposed to the depradations of predators and diseases; and shortages of food and other resources are commonplace. The animal's 'struggle for existence' is against these and other adverse influences in its environment. For a species that is just holding its own in the struggle for existence $R_0 = 1$. Given a sufficiently long time-scale no species is likely to maintain a rate of increase

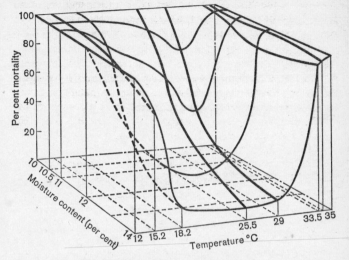

Figure 1. The influence of temperature and moisture on the death-rate in a population of rice weevils living in wheat. Moisture measured as per cent water in grain. Mortality measured through the whole life-cycle.

giving $R_0 = 1$ if only because ecological succession, going on universally, brings change to the environments of all species. But departures from a mean value of 1 for R_0 over any short time (say the span of an ecologist's working life) are usually small relative to the enormous potential indicated by such figures as those in Table 1. For most species a large proportion of the individuals in every generation are doomed to die without leaving progeny or leaving very few progeny. The struggle for existence is intense.

It comes within the scope of population ecology to seek explanations for the discrepancy between the natural rate of increase in the natural population which we may call r and the potential rate of increase R_0 based on the theoretical statistic r_m (the innate capacity for increase). In a fluctuating population the value of r will be sometimes negative, sometimes positive; in a declining population r will be predominantly negative, in an increasing population r will be predominantly positive. The natural rate of increase is a function of two components, the birth rate and the death rate. The birth rate is largely influenced by the speed of development from birth to reproductive maturity and the fecundity of the mature females. So an ecological investigation into the growth and control of natural populations should be made primarily by studying the speed of development of the

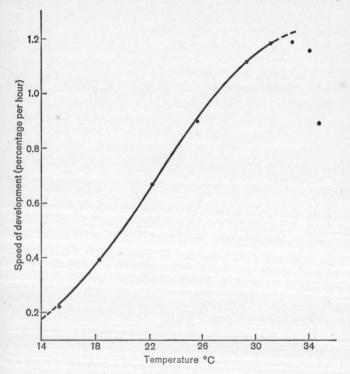

Figure 2. The influence of temperature on the speed of development of rice weevils living in wheat containing 14 per cent water. The figures along the vertical axis show the percentage of the development of an egg (from laying to hatching) completed in one hour.

immature stages of the life cycle, the fecundity (and fertility) of the mature females and the expectation of life for individuals of all stages of the life cycle.

L. C. Birch studied the influence of temperature and humidity on the speed of development, fecundity and longevity of the rice weevil *Calandra oryzae*. The rice weevil, despite its common name, lives mostly in stored wheat in Australia so Birch did his experiments with weevils living in wheat. He controlled the humidity in their environment by controlling the moisture content of the grain in which they were living. The results of his experiments are summarized in Figures 1, 2 and 3. Figure 1 shows that the death-rate was minimal at moderate temperatures (between 18° and 29°C) in moist wheat. But even at the most favourable temperature the death-rate increased to 100 per cent as the moisture content of the grain decreased to 10 per cent; and even in moist grain the death-rate rose steeply at temperatures on either side of the favourable range. Figure 2 shows that in

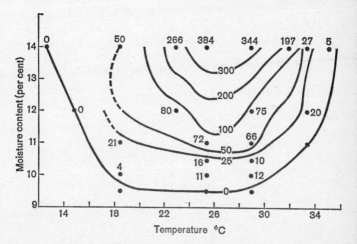

Figure 3. The influence of temperature and moisture on the number of eggs laid by a female rice weevil during its life. The separate figures are actual experimental results. The other figures label the lines of equal fecundity.

moist grain where the survival rate is high the speed of development varied in a sigmoidal way with temperature. Figure 3 shows that the weevils laid most eggs in moist wheat within the range 26°–28°C but the fecundity decreased rapidly as the grain got drier or its temperature moved above or below the rather narrow favourable range. The figures in Table 2 were obtained by using these results to calculate the 'finite rate of increase' (λ) and the 'rate of increase per generation' (R_0, see Table 1).

Table 2. The influence of Temperature and Moisture on the Finite Rate of Increase (λ), and the Rate of Increase per Generation (R_0) of *Calandra oryzae*; λ Measured as Increase per Individual per Week.

Temperature °C	Moisture content of grain, per cent									
	14.0		12.0		11.0		10.5		10.0	
	λ	R_0	λ	R_0	λ	R_0	λ	R_0	λ	R_0
13.0	< <1	< <1	< <1	< <1	< <1	< <1	< <1	< <1	< <1	< <1
15.2	1.01	1.3	<1	<1	<1	<1	<1	<1	< <1	< <1
18.2	1.15	13.8	–	–	1.10	8.9	<1	<1	< <1	< <1
23.0	1.54	15.4	1.35	13.4	–	–	–	–	< <1	< <1
25.5	1.83	41.4	–	–	1.36	9.1	1.07	1.6	< <1	< <1
29.1	2.15	114.0	1.50	12.4	1.42	8.8	0.96	0.8	< <1	< <1
32.3	1.65	25.9	–	–	–	–	<1	<1	< <1	< <1
33.5	1.15	2.6	1.00	1.0	<1	<1	<1	<1	< <1	< <1
34.0	–	< <1	< <1	< <1	< <1	< <1	< <1	< <1	< <1	< <1

Note that at the extremes of temperature and in extremely dry grain the rate of increase is so very much less than one that any population exposed to such extremes of temperature or humidity would quickly die out. In moist grain (14 per cent) a relatively high rate of increase per generation (R_0) can be maintained despite a relatively low rate of increase per week (λ) because of the long generation-time; the converse holds at unfavourably high temperatures. The values for λ and R_0 at 29.1°C and 14 per cent moisture content correspond to the innate capacity for increase (r_m, see Table 1) because these levels of temperature and moisture are optimal. At 33.5°C in grain with 12 per cent moisture R_0

equalled 1 which implies that the population is just replacing itself from generation to generation.

If by chance a natural population of *Calandra oryzae* were living in a place where temperature and humidity were at these levels the numbers in the population would remain steady without the interference of any other restraint such as those exercised by predators, diseases or shortage of food.

Such restraints often, though not invariably, have the quality of a servo-mechanism, that is, they generate a negative feed-back because the intensity of their operation varies directly with the density of the population. Such servo-mechanisms have been given a technical name in ecology; they are called 'density-dependent factors'.

Many ecologists have argued that no explanation for the number of animals in a natural population can be complete or adequate unless it includes a density-dependent factor. The current explosion of human populations gives poignancy to this argument. In populations of non-human species density-dependent factors may operate in diverse ways ranging from starvation, through predation to social stress and aggression. But nowhere in nature can we find a model of a density-dependent process which might be allowed to operate on human populations without causing inestimable misery and distress. The most plausible model is the widespread starvation experienced by *Cactoblastis cactorum* in Queensland after they had denuded the countryside of the prickly pear which is their food and left the habitat bare of food for their posterity. The model is not of course complete because man is not only denuding his habitat of resources but polluting it as well. On the other hand, men already have the knowledge if only they had the wisdom to curb the population explosion and ultimately to reduce the numbers of man, which is so urgently desirable, using density-independent methods which would be relatively painless and perhaps even pleasant.

So let us examine some of the mechanisms of the struggle for existence in populations of non-human animals looking especially for comparisons between density-dependent and density-independent mechanisms, and hoping to uncover some ideas that might be useful in considering human populations.

The Mechanisms of the Struggle for Existence

The animal's struggle for existence may be considered to be a struggle against its environment, which implies that under the heading 'environment' we must consider anything that may influence an animal's chance to survive and to reproduce. In this context the more important components of environment will be seen to include: (1) the weather, (2) predators, parasites, and diseases, (3) food and other resources, (4) other individuals of the same species.

(1) WEATHER

Birch's experiments with *Calandra oryzae* serve to illustrate the way that weather may influence an animal's chance to survive and reproduce. Weather characteristically varies between seasons and also over longer periods so that trends in the natural rate of increase engendered in one season, or run of seasons, may be reversed during the next fluctuation. The rate of increase may fluctuate widely on either side of unity but if the mean is close to unity secular trends in the numbers in the population may be slight, giving the impression over a short period (say the life of an ecologist) of stability.

Another characteristic of weather, clearly illustrated by Birch's experiments, is the existence of an optimum. If, for the purpose of formalizing the relationship between the component of environment and its influence on the animal we plot the animal's chance to survive and reproduce against the 'activity' of the particular component of environment we get for weather the sort of graph shown in Figure 4(a). Activity in these diagrams is measured in the units appropriate for each component of environment – degrees for temperatures, numbers for predators, grams for food and so on. The bell-shaped curve in Figure 4(a) indicates an optimum in the median range decreasing to zero at either extreme.

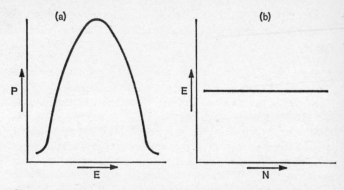

Figure 4. Weather: the curves (a) and (b), taken together illustrate the absence of feed-back. Curve (a) shows the reaction of the animal to its environment; E represents the 'activity' of the environment; P represents the animal's chance to survive and reproduce. Curve (b) shows the reaction of the environment to the density of the population; E represents the same quantity in curve (b) as in curve (a); N represents the density of the population. The reaction in curve (a) is taking place now, but the reaction in curve (b) is spread over the next generation (or cohort).

Yet another important characteristic of weather is that nearly always its activity is independent of the density of the population. This is simply because the weather experienced by an animal is usually caused by events that are remote from and quite unrelated to the density of the population to which the animal belongs. This relationship of density-independence is represented by the horizontal straight line in Figure 4(b); in this diagram the activity of the component of the environment is plotted against the density of the population. Similar sets of graphs can be drawn to illustrate interactions between animals and other components of their environment.

(2) PREDATORS, PARASITES AND DISEASES

Since predators, parasites and diseases are always more or less harmful and since more predators will always press more heavily on the prey than few predators, the graph relating the activity of this component of environment to the animal's chance to survive and to reproduce takes the form of a descending curve as in Figure 5(a). But with predators the reaction of the environment to the density of the population cannot be expressed by a single graph (as in the case of weather) because there are two quite distinct reactions recognizable. For example, consider the predation of the fox on the rabbit in a small Alpine valley in the Snowy Mountains in south-eastern Australia. Both species are introductions from Europe to Australia; both are widely distributed and their relationship to each other differs in different parts of the continent. In this small Alpine valley their relationship serves nicely to illustrate a density-independent reaction between predator and prey. The rabbits have their burrows in the rocky, sloping sides of the valley where the foxes cannot dig them out. The rabbits feed mostly on grasses that grow on the flat floor of the valley. During summer there is always an abundance of green herbage close to their burrows; they can get all the food that they need close to home and run very little risk of being caught by a fox. During winter the valley is covered by snow and the rabbits have to go further afield usually to the banks of a small stream that flows down the middle of the valley where tall grasses and shrubs have their tops above the snow. At this time of the year a rabbit runs a much greater risk of being caught and eaten by a fox; and many of them are eaten.

During summer when rabbits are virtually inaccessible to foxes the foxes feed instead on large wingless grasshoppers which are usually quite abundant at this time of the year. The number of foxes that persist in the area depends largely on the numbers of grasshoppers and only to a negligible extent on the density of the rabbit population.

Another classic example of a density-independent relationship between predator and prey comes from the literature on the biological control of insect pests. The caterpillars of the coconut moth (*Levuana irridescens*) used to be a serious pest on coconut palms in Fiji. During a serious outbreak it was usual to find virtually every palm defoliated. About 1925 a fly (*Ptychomyia remota*) the larvae of which prey on the caterpillars of the coconut moth was introduced into Fiji. *Ptychomyia* possesses the characters of a 'successful' predator: it breeds more rapidly than its prey; and its powers of dispersal are incomparably greater than those of *Levuana*. Its success as an agent of biological control was immediate and thorough: within a year *Levuana* had become, and has remained every since, a rare insect. Nevertheless the success of *Ptychomyia* depended on a third link in the ecological chain.

Only caterpillars that have reached an advanced stage of development are suitable prey of *Ptychomyia*. In the absence of the predators, or in the early stages of an outbreak, it is usual to find a substantial overlapping of generations; all stages of the life cycle are present including the advanced caterpillars that serve *Ptychomyia*. In the declining stages of an outbreak the overlapping of generations tends to disappear and there comes a time when there are no caterpillars present in a suitable stage for *Ptychomyia*. The adults of *Ptychomyia* live no more than 10 days; quite a large proportion of the predators may die without reproducing if the period when no caterpillars of a suitable stage are present should be prolonged for several weeks.

In most parts of Fiji this circumstance mattered not at all to *Ptychomyia* because there lived in the 'bush' surrounding the coconut groves two species of caterpillars that served as alternative sources of food for *Ptychomyia*. *Ptychomyia* persisted on this food until *Levuana*, which it preferred, was again present in a suitable condition.

But on one Fijian island where these alternative sources of food were absent the predators periodically experienced an extreme shortage of food and they became extremely scarce. At these times the *Levuana* were able to multiply greatly before the predators caught up with them again. So in this island periodic outbreaks of *Levuana* continued to occur despite the presence of the predator *Ptychomyia*.

The essential point of this story is that on the main island of Fiji the predators were able to maintain high numbers and hence maintain heavy pressure on their preferred prey because there was an abundant alternative source of food that they could turn to when the preferred prey was scarce. The abundance of the predators depended largely on the supply of alternative food and only negligibly on the density of the population of *Levuana*, the preferred prey.

Another variation on the same theme is provided by the incidence of malaria among certain villagers in Malaya. Men live in clearings along the banks of a river and monkeys live in the tree tops in the surrounding jungle. Mosquitoes may bite both men and monkeys. The abundance of malaria depends chiefly on the densities of the populations of monkeys and mosquitoes and the chance that a man will become infected depends largely on the densities of the populations of these two species and hardly at all on the density of his own population.

These three examples illustrate a phenomenon that is commonplace in nature. The general principle is that when a predator has a preferred prey but also has an adequate supply of an alternative source of food to fall back on when the preferred prey becomes scarce then the activity of the predator as a component in the environment of the prey is largely independent of the density of the prey. The relationship is expressed by the horizontal straight line in Figure 5(b).

The situation is quite different when the predator is restricted to one species of prey. Ecologists have a special name for this sort of predation: they call it *obligate* because the predator is *obliged* to stick to one species of prey. Obligate predation very rarely, if ever, occurs when the predator is a vertebrate; it can be found occasionally in invertebrates, especially insects, and also in certain disease-causing organisms and their hosts.

It so happens that the first success in the biological control of an insect pest was achieved with an obligate predator. The story is worth recounting not only as an example of a density-dependent reaction between predator and prey but also because of its historical interest. About 160 years ago a scale insect (*Icerya purchasi*), which in Australia lives naturally on various species of *Acacia*, was accidentally introduced into California where it became established on citrus. By 1890 it had spread and multiplied so enormously that it threatened to destroy the citrus industry in Southern California. About 1887 an American entomologist, searching in Australia for 'natural enemies' of *Icerya* discovered the ladybird (*Rodolia cardinalis*). In 1888 a colony of 129 ladybirds was established inside a cage that had been built over an orange tree carrying a dense population of the scale insects. Within a year the ladybirds had increased enormously inside the cage and had destroyed most of the scale insects. The cage was removed. Within 3 months *Rodolia* had spread through the orchard and eaten most of the *Icerya* that were in it. This success was repeated elsewhere in Southern California and ever since there have been few *Icerya* there. The scale insects have not been killed out altogether because Southern California is a large place and there are always a few colonies of *Icerya* that manage to become established and to live for a while before the predators find them. If by chance, perhaps because of a run of unseasonable weather, these colonies become larger or more numerous temporarily, then they are more easily found by predators, which, given more food, increase temporarily and, pressing more heavily on their prey, reduce the numbers of *Icerya* to the very low level that is characteristic of their numbers in this region.

The control of the European rabbit in Australia by the virus disease *myxomatosis* has some points in common with the control of *Icerya* in California by the ladybird *Rodolia*, but more important, it resembles the control of *Levuana* by *Ptychomyia* in Fiji. The rabbit was introduced to Australia in 1859. As so often happens when a virile species is first introduced into a new and favourable country the rabbit increased in numbers very quickly indeed: it seemed almost as if the population was growing quite free of any restraint and realizing its full innate capacity for increase. At the same time the rabbits spread across the countryside with incredible speed, colonizing as they went, just as the scale insect *Icerya* had done in California. It is not known how numerous the original colony was but F. N. Ratcliffe wrote of 'a small shipment' from England that was released near Geelong in southern Victoria. By 1880 they had crossed the River Murray 200 miles to the north; by 1886 they had crossed the boundary between New South Wales and Queensland a further 500 miles in the same direction. Spreading in a westerly direction the rabbits reached Fowlers Bay in South

Australia (750 miles from Geelong) in 1892; and they reached Geraldton on the west coast of Western Australia (1,800 miles from Geelong) in 1907. Meanwhile they continued to thrive and to increase in most of the country they had colonized. Driving along a country road as dusk was approaching one might see rabbits scampering on the roadsides in their scores and hundreds. One estimate placed the number of rabbits in south-eastern Australia at between 40,000,000 and 50,000,000 in 1949 before the great panzootic of myxomatosis began in 1950.

The virus of myxomatosis is specific to rabbits: no other species of animal in Australia is susceptible. The virus exists in a number of strains the most virulent of which causes a disease which almost always kills the rabbit within a week or so. Such a strain of the virus was introduced into Australia from South America in 1950. Fortunately, widespread rains during 1951 and 1952 favoured the breeding, in large numbers and over wide areas, of the mosquitoes which are vectors of the myxomatosis virus. With dense populations of rabbits and mosquitoes and with the virus already established in the area and spreading along the waterways the stage was set for a great panzootic. The disease spread through the rabbits like wild-fire killing them in their millions. Over millions of acres, rabbits were exterminated or reduced to extremely low numbers. Remnants of the population persisted here and there but nowhere with the density that prevailed before the panzootic.

With the number of rabbits so few farmers were able, by using mechanical and chemical measures, to prevent the rabbits from breeding on their farms. But elsewhere in local situations small groups of rabbits began to multiply. Invariably they would be discovered before long by a disease-carrying mosquito and an outbreak of myxomatosis would reduce their numbers again, but usually not so dramatically as in the original outbreak because the virus was no longer as virulent as it had been, and the rabbits were less susceptible.

Because the time required for a generation of the virus of myxomatosis is very short, comparable with that required by bacteria and other micro-organisms, there has been ample time

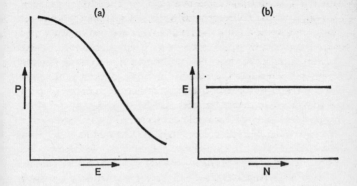

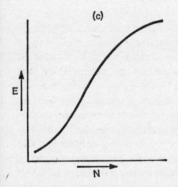

Figure 5. Predators, parasites and diseases. The same conventions apply as in Figure 4. The curve in B represents those situations in which there is no feed-back. The curves in (a) and (c), sloping in opposite directions indicate a negative feed-back between the density of the population and the environment (see text).

for the 'long-term' evolutionary consequences of the struggle for existence to be observed during the few years since the virulent virus was let go in 1950. The virus has evolved towards a less virulent strain which kills a smaller proportion of the infected rabbits leaving those that recover immune just as a child that has recovered from measles remains immune to measles. The consequences of outbreaks of myxomatosis are not now so severe as they were originally but they still serve to prevent the rabbits from increasing in the way that they used to do in the absence of myxomatosis. Despite the evolutionary changes in its virulence the virus remains an obligate 'predator' of the rabbit, but, unlike *Rodolia*, myxomatosis does not generate a negative feedback because the activity of myxomatosis depends chiefly on the abundance of its vectors. The abundance in mosquitoes that transmit the disease depends chiefly on the weather and only slightly on the abundance of the rabbits. The reaction is represented by the horizontal line in Figure 5(c).

(3) FOOD AND OTHER RESOURCES

An animal's chance to survive and multiply is enhanced by an abundance of food and other resources so the graph representing the influence of this component of environment on the animal must be an ascending curve as in Figure 6(a).

But the influence of the density of the population on the activity of this component of environment may differ according to circumstances, being sometimes density-dependent and sometimes density-independent. Let us examine the circumstances in which these two reactions may occur.

Animals that get their food by harvesting or grazing living plants or preying on living animals cannot afford to exploit their resources without restraint because over-exploiting may lead to a smaller crop for the next generation. This principle is so familiar in the annals of farming, animal husbandry and fisheries (e.g. whales) that there is no need to dwell on it.

The history of a herd of deer that inhabited the Kaibab Plateau in Arizona illustrates the principle. In 1907 the deer lived surrounded by plenty of food because other pressures in the environment kept their numbers few relative to the supply of food; there were about 4,000 deer at this time although the area might have supported 30,000 without detriment to the food. This condition persisted until about 1918. About this time changes in the management of the range-land, a deliberate campaign to destroy certain predators and other changes in the environment allowed the deer to multiply greatly. By 1925 they had increased to 100,000. Such enormous numbers over-exploited the stock of food, denuding and ravaging the range to such a degree that by 1940 it could support no more than 10,000 deer.

In the preceding section I referred to *Rodolia* as a predator of *Icerya*. But I might instead have looked at the other side of the coin and considered *Rodolia* as a carnivorous animal depending on *Icerya* for food. In 1889 *Rodolia* found itself surrounded by an abundance of food; it multiplied without restraint and came to over-exploit its stocks of food so heavily that the *Icerya* could no longer maintain themselves except at a very low level of abundance. As a consequence, although *Rodolia* still exists in California, it has remained scarce ever since the beginning.

The general rule which is illustrated by these two examples is that when an animal depends on living plants or animals for its food there is a density-dependent interaction between the numbers of animals and the activity of their food which can be represented by a descending curve as in Figure 6(c). Indeed the rule is more general than this because it applies to any living resources, not only food.

There is a very important class of exceptions to this rule which is best illustrated by reference to the paradoxical situation in which the sheep tick (*Ixodes ricinus*) characteristically runs a high chance of starving to death surrounded by a great abundance of food. The sheep tick feeds by sucking the blood of sheep. It requires three years to grow to maturity. Once a year it emerges from cover near the ground where it has been sheltering and climbs to an exposed grass-stem where it lies in wait for a passing sheep. It can maintain this position for about a week. If a sheep brushes the grass-stem the tick will cling to the sheep while it engorges itself with blood and then drop off; it will seek shelter near the

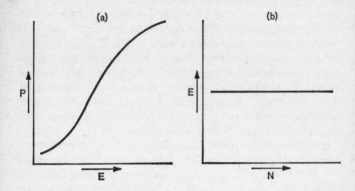

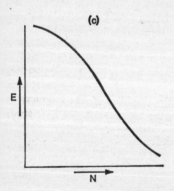

Figure 6. Resources. The same conventions apply as in Figure 4. The curve in (b) represents those situations in which there is no feed-back. The curves in (a) and (c), sloping in opposite directions, indicate a negative feed-back between the density of the population and the environment (see text).

ground where it will rest for a year while it digests its large meal of blood and prepares itself for its annual meal to be taken at the same time next year.

The number of sheep may vary from less than one to several per acre but there is never enough to give a tick much chance of getting a meal. So most ticks die of starvation not because they have used up all their food (they have in fact reduced it scarcely at all) but because they could not reach it. The numbers of sheep may depend on a variety of causes (such as rainfall and the fertility of the soil which influences the growth of the pasture) none of which depends on the density of the tick population. So there is no interaction between the density of the tick population and the activity of their food which is indicated by the horizontal straight line in Figure 6(b). This sort of food shortage is called a 'relative shortage'; it represents a situation which is often found in nature. Some anthropologists think that it may have been the chief limiting factor for populations of neolithic man.

Animals whose habit of feeding puts them into the large class of scavengers (for example, blow-fly maggots feeding on the carcasses of rabbits) will as a rule exert no influence on the supply of food for the next generation. For example, the blowflies will influence neither the density of the rabbit population nor the death-rate among the rabbits. So the relationship between the scavenger and its food will also be represented by the horizontal straight line in Figure 6(b).

(4) OTHER ANIMALS OF THE SAME SPECIES

Certain species of animals mostly to be found among the birds and small mammals possess elaborate patterns of social behaviour characterized by a ritual of aggressive acts directed against individuals of the same species which may deprive the weaker or less resolute individuals of their opportunity to breed or perhaps even to survive. Perhaps the simplest and best understood of these sorts of behaviour patterns is territorial behaviour in birds.

For example, H. N. Kluijver described how the great tits (*Parus major*) in a wood in Arnhem would come together in pairs during autumn when the season's crop of young birds were approaching maturity and each pair would defend a territory by song and ritualistic display – a sort of psychological warfare. The losers in these battles would abandon the territory and in doing so would abandon their chance of having a secure place to spend the winter or a good place for breeding in the spring. The territory that is defended usually contains more than the minimum requirements of one pair for nesting, sheltering and feeding. So this sort of behaviour seems to place a restraint on the size of the population, especially on the breeding population, which is independent of all the components of environment except the numbers of other individuals of the same species. The interaction between the animal and its environment is clearly density-dependent and can be represented by the curves in Figures 7(a) and 7(b).

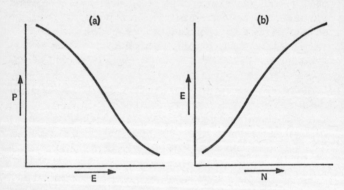

Figure 7. Other individuals of the same species. The same conventions apply as in Figure 4. The curves (a) and (b), sloping in opposite directions, indicate a negative feed-back between the density of the population and the environment (see text).

The Control of Natural Populations

Looking back over Figures 4 to 7 one can see that the (a) curves which represent the influence of the environment on the animal's chance to survive and reproduce may slope either up or down.

The (b) and (c) curves which represent the responses of the environment to the density of the population may either have no slope, indicating no reaction with density, or they may slope in the opposite direction from the (a) curves indicating that the reaction to density is a negative feed-back like the servo-mechanism in the governor of a steam engine. Theoretically a negative feed-back would be expected to depress the growth of a large population and to stimulate the growth of a small one thus keeping the population between certain limits as a governor keeps the speed of the steam engine between certain limits.

I have not mentioned the circumstances in which the (a) curves slope in the same direction as the (c) curves indicating a positive feed-back with density. Such situations do arise and are important in natural populations of non-human animals but there is no space to deal with them in this short discussion. They are in any case more important in relation to the extinction of populations than in relation to the control of populations.

The densities of a number of natural populations that have been carefully studied have been shown to be controlled by density-independent reactions, while for others density-dependent reactions seem to be more important. It is generally accepted as a truism by ecologists that any natural population, no matter for how long or how thoroughly it seems to be controlled by density-independent restraints, has the potential, if the density-independent restraints are lifted, to increase to a level at which density-dependent restraints might be expected to take over. But to recognize this potential is not to say that density-dependent restraints must be prominent or present in the circumstances of all natural populations. On the contrary, experience suggests that it is the natural condition of most species of animals to be rare and to be kept rare by the struggle for existence with an environment in which density-independent restraints are the most important limiting factors. Apart from weather the density-independent restraints that turn up most frequently are probably a relative shortage of food (or some other resource) and predation by a predator that has alternative sources of food.

The curve in Figure 8 suggests that our own population is

irrupting in much the same way as the populations of *Rodolia* in California and the deer on the Kaibab Plateau irrupted when they had plenty of food and in the absence of any other restraint. Unless man takes political and social action to restrain the growth of his own population (thereby demonstrating that in the matter of intelligence he really is different from the non-human animals) the growth and control of human populations must be expected to conform to the same principles that govern populations of non-human species. Looking at the array of density-dependent reactions that are known to operate on non-human

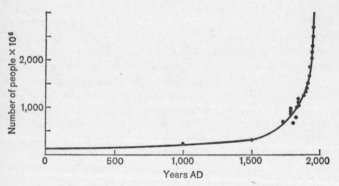

Figure 8. Growth of the human population. Similar irruptions in the numbers of several species of non-human animals are mentioned in the text.

populations one cannot visualize any that would not be cruel and horrible if allowed to operate freely on a human population. The only alternative (apart from the unutterably terrible one of conniving at World War III) is for man to devise and to impose, by political and social measures, density-independent restraints on the increase of his own population that would cause a decline from the current numbers down to some number, much below today's total, which would allow a comfortable and secure existence for animals fortunate enough to belong to such a rational species.

Bibliography

Browning, T. O., *Animal Populations*, Hutchinson, 1963.

Elton, C. S., *The Ecology of Invasions by Plants and Animals*, Methuen, 1958.

Lack, D., *Population Studies of Birds*, Clarendon Press, 1966.

Odum, E. P., *Ecology*, Holt, Rinehart & Winston, New York, 1963.

Bird Populations

Christopher Perrins

Stability of Numbers

It is a commonplace that bird populations are relatively stable; the species which are often observed breeding in gardens, such as the robin and the thrush, are present each year in rather similar numbers. Naturally, there are exceptions, but careful censuses support this general observation. Some examples of such records are shown in Figures 1–3.

Each of the populations shown in these figures contained a similar number of breeding pairs at the beginning and the end of the study period (the low numbers in the first year of the tit study were probably due to the very severe winter of 1946–7). Over the duration of the studies, however, each has shown changes in numbers. The year-to-year variations in the two species of tits have been considerable. In addition, both usually fluctuated in parallel suggesting that they are affected similarly by changes in the environment. As a rule, the numbers of the heron have changed much less markedly than those of the tits between one year and the next, but from time to time there has been a sharp decrease followed by an almost equally rapid increase. The reason for the decreases is well known: in cold winters many rivers and other waters become frozen and hence the heron cannot catch its fish. The graphs for the two populations show a marked tendency to vary in parallel. This was to be expected since the winter weather is usually similar in both areas. In the same way, high numbers of tits and other species tend to occur in different parts of western Europe in the same years. The numbers of storks show smaller changes from year to year; this may be partly because they are migrants, coming to Europe only to breed, and that there is less variation in the climate of the areas in which they spend the winter. The numbers of storks also show slow long-term changes, perhaps due to man's alteration of the habitat. In any area, greater changes than these occur over very long periods of time, with the extinction of some species and colonizations by others. At present many changes in bird numbers are due to man's alteration of the habitat, but similar changes occur, though usually more slowly, for natural reasons, and no avifauna has survived long periods without change.

Potential Power of Increase

It is easy to convince people that the numbers of birds are usually stable; it is equally easy to calculate that theoretically this need not always be so. Nearly all species of animals produce large numbers of young and, if all of these survived, each population would increase at a fantastic rate. Birds have a relatively small reproductive potential compared with many of the lower animals, for instance most common songbirds, such as robins, blackbirds and tits, lay around 10 eggs per pair per year. With no deaths this would mean that one pair would give rise to 6 pairs in the following year (or 7,776 pairs after only 5 seasons). One does not need accurate measurements to be sure that this is not happening.

There are, however, occasions when an increase in numbers can be extremely rapid; these usually occur when an animal or plant arrives in a new habitat where it can flourish. Some of the more famous (or infamous) of these are not birds: the rabbit and the prickly pear in Australia, the grey squirrel in England. However, some birds have made equally dramatic conquests. The starling was introduced into the United States in 1890 and 1891 when 120 to 160 were released in New York. By the mid-1940s they had reached the westernmost states and the original number were estimated to have increased a millionfold by 1948. The house sparrow was introduced into New York in 1850 and within about fifty years had been recorded in all the states of the Union, in

Mexico and Canada. The actual numbers of this species are less well recorded, but there must be very many millions.

The starling and house sparrow were introduced by man, but colonization can be natural. In the early part of this century, the cattle egret bred only in Spain and parts of west Africa and southern Asia. It was first found breeding in the New World, in British Guiana, in about 1930. Since then it has spread along the coast of South America, through central America and into many of the southern states of the United States. It was first recorded in Florida in about 1941 and by 1955 there were several thousand there. The collared dove has recently spread across Europe and into Britain. First recorded breeding in 1955, its number in 1964 was estimated at almost 20,000. The fulmar, a species which does not breed until it is 7 or 8 years old, and then produces only one young each year, bred in Britain only on St Kilda until 1878 when it first bred on Foula in Shetland. By 1959 there were 100,000 occupied nest sites in Britain (excluding St Kilda).

Increases of fulmar and collared dove have probably been aided by further immigration, but this is not likely to have been an important factor in the cattle egret, the starling or the house sparrow.

A further well-documented introduction is that of the pheasant on to Protection Island in the state of Washington. Figure 4 shows spring and autumn counts for 6 years after pairs had been put on the island. Even this dramatic increase was not as fast as is theoretically possible, since marked losses occurred in winter.

Such great changes occur only when there is suitable land at present unoccupied by the animal in question. However, big increases sometimes occur where species are well-established. In 4 of the 5 graphs in Figures 1–3 an increase of more than 50 per cent was sometimes recorded between one year and the next. In these cases, however, a change of this order does not normally occur over a number of years in succession. In tits it rarely occurs in two successive years, while a rapid increase of heron occurs only in years after a severe winter has reduced their numbers: when numbers are back to normal no further increase occurs.

Mortality and Average Age

The reason why birds do not normally increase rapidly is, of course, because large numbers of them die. Many people are still inclined to doubt that the actual death-rates are so high. It is of passing interest to note that the huge losses of animals that occur in nature was one of Darwin's central points in his theory of natural selection; without a very high 'wastage' it would have been harder for him to postulate the natural selection.

In fact, in the case of small songbirds such as robins, only some 50 per cent of the breeding adults from one season live to breed in the following one; this means that on average, one member of each pair dies each year. Clearly therefore in a stable population one young per pair (and no more) must survive to replace the dying adult. In species such as those which lay 10 eggs or more a year it follows that 90 per cent of these do not live to become adults. In birds, the highest known death-rates occur in small species of songbirds, the adults of most other species have a lower annual mortality and they also usually produce fewer young. However, the proportion of young which survive to breed is not necessarily larger. The Manx shearwater – a gull-sized seabird related to the Albatrosses – breeds on islands round the coast of Britain. It lays only 1 egg each year. The adult has a long expectancy of life, with an annual mortality of 4 per cent or less, which means that it can expect to live for 25 years. It can easily be calculated therefore that, in a stable population, less than 10 per cent of the eggs laid produce birds that live long enough to breed. Hence the difference between the parent tit and the parent shearwater is that the tit produces on average one breeding bird from 10 eggs in one year and the shearwater one from 10 eggs in 10 years; only the time scale is different.

The graphs in Figure 5 show some examples of what would happen in a population of songbirds where fewer than 50 per cent of the adults or fewer than 90 per cent of the young died each year. These theoretical curves are plotted against the figures for the great tit from Figure 1. Even a small increase in the survival rates produces an inexorable rise in numbers.

The stage at which the annual losses occur is not well known. One of the main reasons for this is that so few dead birds are found in nature; the bodies are quickly consumed by other animals. In many species the period in the nest is very dangerous, but in hole-nesting species such as the great tit or the tawny owl the young are relatively safe in the nest, and the highest losses probably occur just after they have left their parents and are learning to fend for themselves; and in temperate regions this is well before, not during, the winter, when one might have expected the heaviest losses. For adults too the summer is more dangerous than might be expected. There are few reliable measurements, but for the blackbird and the great tit adult losses seem to be about equal between the 6 summer and the 6 winter months.

The large number of deaths each year are not apparent in graphs such as those in Figures 1–3, as these show only the changes in numbers of breeding birds from one year to another. Figure 6 shows the changes within a year superimposed on the breeding numbers. Such figures are not purely hypothetical, and field observations of several species (grouse, pigeon, blackbird, great tit) show close agreement with theoretical expectations.

If the numbers of breeding birds in a population are to remain stable over a long period the numbers of birds that die must be equal to the numbers that are produced. It does not follow, however, that an exact balance will be found in every year. In different years at Oxford, the survival of young great tits from the time that they leave the nest until the autumn has varied between 0·3 and 4·0 young per pair. This large variation is the main reason for the sharp fluctuations in the breeding population shown in Figure 1. There are probably equally large annual variations in the production of surviving young in other species, but with the notable exception of some game birds, few figures are available. In general the young of the highly productive small species seem to show the greatest variations in success, and correspondingly these birds show some of the greatest annual fluctuations in number.

Since so few dead birds are found, some writers have attempted to explain the high losses of young that occur not as deaths, but as movement out of one area into another where the density of birds is lower. While there is, of course, some movement of young from one place to another, results from ringing suggest that it is very unusual for young of most species to settle far from their birth place. Further, they are not found in great numbers in the areas to which it is supposed that they moved. Besides this, as mentioned earlier, in many species breeding success and population changes tend to be similar over wide areas in the same years. Hence a 'surplus' of young birds cannot be accommodated in areas elsewhere since these areas will also have a surplus. It follows that the high losses of young birds cannot easily be interpreted as some form of movement; death is the inevitable cause.

There are also variations in the annual mortality of adult birds, but these are usually very much smaller than the variation in the mortality of the young. For example the annual mortality of adult great tits near Oxford has varied between about 40 per cent and about 60 per cent. Again, although there are few long series of measurements the larger species seem to have not only a lower annual mortality, but also a less variable one.

The lives of adult birds are usually described in terms of percentage survival or percentage mortality or death-rate. The average life expectancy of an adult of a small bird with a 50 per cent mortality is only 1·5 years, whereas that of a large seabird such as a gannet or a shearwater, with an annual mortality of 5 or 4 per cent, is 20 to 25 years.

In man, the expectation of further life depends greatly on the present age of the individual concerned, but this is not usually so in birds, and once the dangerous period of immaturity is passed, the expectation of further life does not appear to change with increasing age. The life expectancy of a bird is compared with that of man in Figure 7. Here the difference between the two species in the number of deaths of very old individuals can be clearly seen. The proportion of wild birds that die of 'old age' must be extremely small, and in fact an increase in death-rate with increase in age has not yet been shown convincingly. The main difficulty is a practical one, that extremely large numbers of birds must be ringed if enough are to be still alive when senility approaches to measure the death-rate; as yet not enough have been ringed. The effects of senility might perhaps be important in the really long-lived birds like certain seabirds. However, it is clear that in most species deaths from old age are of negligible importance in the regulation of numbers.

How Numbers are Controlled (1: Reproduction)

Clearly there is a close correlation between the numbers of births and of deaths in a stable population. However, there has been, and still is, considerable dispute as to whether stability in populations is brought about by alterations in the numbers of births which compensate for the average death-rate or whether the latter is the result of an earlier birth-rate. It may be thought that this is not a very important issue, but the mechanisms postulated as necessary to bring about the limitation of numbers have fundamentally different (and opposing) bases. Further, to be able to control or protect species one must be clear about the factors which regulate their numbers.

The opposing schools of thought have been most clearly stated by Lack and Wynne-Edwards; for those interested in following the arguments further, there are references in the bibliography. Lack's view is that the birds are breeding as fast as they can: the number of young per brood has been fixed by natural selection as the maximum the species can successfully raise under local conditions. If more eggs are laid and hatched there would be less food per young bird followed by starvation and fewer (rather than more) surviving young. The large increase in numbers after breeding results in subsequent severe competition for food outside the breeding season and many deaths, leaving a population much the same size as before.

In contrast, Wynne-Edwards suggests that birds have evolved reproductive rates that will not lead to great increases in numbers, so avoiding over-exploitation of the food supply. To prevent over-exploitation, Wynne-Edwards claims, the birds produce approximately the number of surviving young that are needed to replace the adult losses. The factors evolved to achieve this end include: a smaller clutch-size; the tendency for some birds not to breed at all in some years; delayed maturity (failure of birds to breed until they are several years old); failure to replace an egg if it is lost, and in some species a reproductive period so long that parents have time to raise only one brood in two years.

These various characteristics are found in certain birds, especially in the long-lived species, such as some seabirds and the larger birds of prey. There are two main difficulties concerning Wynne-Edwards's views. First, if a particular bird 'cheats', because it has a mutation allowing it to reproduce more rapidly than the rest, it will contribute more offspring than the rest to the ensuing generations, and hence, being favoured by natural selection will become steadily more common. To overcome this difficulty, Wynne-Edwards has produced a theory of group selection. The individuals in a population with a slow reproductive rate do not over-eat their food reserves, so survive and replace those populations which overproduce and therefore become extinct through starvation. There is no evidence that this happens, and as it runs contrary to classical Darwinian selection (which acts through the individuals) the burden of proof is on Wynne-Edwards.

Secondly, most of Wynne-Edwards' ideas are not open to experimental testing. It is not, for example, possible to discover whether a fulmar, which does not normally breed until the age of 7 to 8, can breed successfully at 4. In one case however, there is a chance of experimental tests – it is possible to alter the brood size at hatching to determine the success of parents with different numbers of young. In the majority of species young added to the brood at hatching are accepted by the parents as if they were their own; there is no evidence which suggests that the birds can recognize their own young at this stage.

In two such studies made at Oxford, using the swift and the great tit, it has been shown that parents raise fewer young if they are given larger broods than the usual one. It is true that, when presented with a larger brood, the parents worked harder to feed them and made more visits with food. However, the increase of effort was not proportionate to the increase in the number of young, so that individual young in large broods had less food than those in smaller broods.

The normal clutch of the swift is 2 or 3. Parents depend for food on small airborne insects and spiders whose availability depends markedly on the summer weather. In a fine summer the parents can find plenty of food and in these seasons, broods of three young produce more survivors than broods of 2. However, in a poor summer when food is short, the individual young in broods of three get too little food and some of them starve. This rarely happens in broods of 2, from which the parents may raise, on average about 1·8 young whereas those with 3 young may raise only about 1·5 young. Therefore, in some summers 3 is the most productive brood, in others 2. Exceedingly rarely in Britain, but a little more commonly on the Continent (where the food supply is better) clutches and broods of 4 have been recorded. At Oxford we made broods of four artificially by adding a newly hatched chick to a brood which was just hatching. The success of these

Table 1 Survival of young swifts in relation to brood-size.

Year	Brood-size	Number of broods	Number raised per brood
1958	2	21	1·95
	3	4	2·75
	4	2	2·0
1959	2	15	2·0
	3	4	3·0
	4	4	2·75
1960	2	18	1·9
	3	6	2·3
	4	5	1·2
1961	2	18	1·95
	3	6	2·3
	4	5	1·4

broods is shown in Table 1. More young were always lost from broods of 4 than from broods of 3. Even in the exceptionally fine summer of 1959, when no other young were lost, so many young died in the broods of 4 that they ended up with fewer young per brood than broods of 3. Hence one can see why any tendency for swifts to lay clutches of four will be almost completely eliminated in Britain. The swift cannot raise more young than it does.

The situation in the great tit is slightly different since few young die in the nest. However, the young of the large broods get less food and leave the nest lighter in weight than those in smaller broods. By trapping the young after they have become independent of their parents, it is possible to show that more of the heavy than of the light young survive. Occasionally, many young from the large broods have survived, but broods of normal size have been as productive as, or more productive than, the large ones in 5 out of 7 years of study. In different years during the study, the most productive brood-size has varied from 6 to 15; this presumably explains why clutches of great tits still vary so in size. No one size has been successful so often that birds which laid clutches of other sizes have been eliminated by natural selection.

Few such experimental manipulations of brood-size have been made, but in one case, that of the gannet, the results are not in accord with those described above. The gannet lays only 1 egg, but if a pair is given a second chick at hatching, it raises both successfully, and when both leave the nest each is nearly as heavy as the single chicks of other pairs. The reason for this is not understood, but the gannet, like several other seabirds, has been increasing rapidly in numbers since the latter half of the 19th century. Hence it seems reasonable to assume that their food has been relatively abundant during this period. It may be, therefore, that recently the gannet has been able to find sufficient food to raise two young whereas previously it has not. Fifty or 100 years is of course a very short time on an evolutionary scale and if a genotype of gannet appeared which laid two eggs it would take very much longer than this for it to spread through a large population of birds whose average life-span is of the order of 20–30 years.

Not only is there evidence, therefore, that birds are producing as many young as they can, but there is also good evidence that some species have second (or even third) broods when they can. In this way the production of young is still further increased. In general, only small birds and some other land birds raise more than one brood in a year. Species such as the blackbird prolong their normal breeding season by breeding either earlier or later than usual whenever conditions permit. In this species the prerequisite for successful breeding is soft ground from which worms can be easily obtained. A mild late February and early March will result in birds starting to breed early and wet weather in June and early July will result in prolonged breeding. Likewise two species of owl, the short-eared and the barn, which are normally single brooded, may raise a second brood when small mammals are exceptionally abundant. Here again the birds are extending their breeding seasons and therefore maximizing their production of young.

How Numbers are Controlled (2: Death)

If the reproductive rate has not been evolved to balance the mortality, the death-rate must in the long-term be a consequence of the numbers of young produced. The balance is only approximate in any one year since, as already mentioned, bird populations fluctuate in numbers from year to year. But they do so only within narrow limits about a mean. Populations of the same species tend to fluctuate in parallel in different areas. However, they may do so round very different densities. Great tits, for instance, are usually found at densities of about 1 pair in each $1\frac{1}{2}$–3 acres of deciduous woodland, whereas in coniferous woodland there is only 1 pair in 6–15 acres.

If a population fluctuates about a given level, it follows that the number must tend to decrease when they are above that level and to increase when they are below it. This concept of density-dependent regulation was originated by Lotka and Volterra in the 1920s and expanded by A. J. Nicholson in the 1930s. In its simplest form the theory implies that the survival rates of individuals is adversely affected by the presence of increasing numbers of its own species in the environment. For example, when there are more birds than usual, the competition for food is more severe and a higher proportion of the population fails to obtain sufficient and so perishes. When the population is normal, the individual bird finds it easier to get enough of the food and so a higher proportion of them survive. Hence whatever the numbers, the population tends to return to the normal level.

Using this concept it is possible to explain the changes in numbers of the heron (Figure 2). When the rivers freeze over in winter the food supply is scarce and so numbers are reduced; after the thaw numbers are low and so each bird encounters less competition for food and has a higher chance of survival. Numbers therefore increase until the previous level is reached when competition becomes sufficiently severe for mortality to increase and numbers to stabilize.

Density-dependent mortality is a simple concept, but it is far from easy to demonstrate that it is occurring in the field. This is partly because few long-term studies of birds have been made, but partly also because in birds (though not in all other animals) the factor most commonly believed to be critical is food and the food supply is extremely hard to measure. For one thing the amount of food may vary markedly from year to year. In Figure 1 the numbers of tits tend to 'see-saw'; the increases in numbers of birds usually occur when there is a good supply of beech seed in the winter and the decreases when the winter food supply is poor. Hence very accurate measurements of the food supply must be made before the changes in numbers of birds can be examined critically.

Food is probably the only factor which can cause the numbers of birds to fluctuate within fairly narrow limits. Other important factors which affect the numbers of birds, such as predators, disease, adverse climatic conditions or accidents, may kill large numbers. However, while the first two could theoretically be related to the density of birds, there is no evidence that they have important density-dependent effects on wild populations. The heron, for example, may be reduced in numbers by bad winter weather, but numbers return to normal as soon as there is a mild winter or a series of mild winters.

Man's Effect on Numbers of Birds

There is a corollary of the theory of density-dependent regulation which is important for man as well as for birds. Because of the high rate of production, once the breeding season is over, there are usually many more birds in a population than can survive on the available food supply. Hence, if a bird which was likely to survive is removed from a population, another that would otherwise have perished will survive in its place. It may therefore be extremely difficult to reduce the numbers of a bird permanently. This has been, and still is, frequently overlooked by those wishing to reduce or eliminate a bird pest.

In the first 3 months of 1963 Europe had very severe weather, which made this the coldest winter for almost 200 years. Large areas were snow-covered for periods of up to 8 weeks. Species such as the bullfinch, which feed largely on ash seeds on the trees above the snow, had plenty of food and so the cold did not effect them greatly. However, some species did suffer severe losses; amongst these, the green woodpecker, the wren and the long-tailed tit were almost exterminated in many areas. There was talk in some quarters of trying to provide extra legal protection for even the common species until they had recovered in numbers. In fact almost all the affected species were back to normal numbers within a year and even the 3 species mentioned above were back in most of their normal haunts within 3 or 4 years. Again, presumably this is because birds have high rates of survival in times of low density.

Bounties have often been offered by governments as an incentive to farmers and others to reduce pest species. From the biological point of view (rather than the political), these have seldom produced any result. A few large birds of prey and some large predatory mammals, which anyway were relatively scarce, have been reduced or even eliminated by shooting, but this does not hold for many other species. R. K. Murton in his book on the wood pigeon makes this point clearly. There has been a grant towards pigeon clearance in the form of 50 per cent of the cost of cartridges. Murton showed that in his study area there were about 63 pigeons per 100 acres at the start of the breeding season; by autumn there were 154. Intensive shooting in late winter removed about 20 birds per hundred acres, but there were still 72 (or 9 more than the previous spring) in early spring. These additional birds died and the numbers at the start of the breeding season were again 63 per 100 acres.

Here, even with intensive shooting, the numbers did not diminish. Even if it were possible to reduce the numbers to a level below that of the previous breeding season, little would be achieved since, by the end of the breeding season, the numbers would be back to the previous level once more. Hence in the main, shooting does not reduce the numbers of birds in a population and even if it does, there is no long-term effect unless the pressure is maintained year after year.

In general, it seems likely that this can be said of most pest species. For example, Ward has shown that the quelea, a small grain-eating bird which is a serious pest in parts of Africa, is no less common now than it was before 'control' methods were started, although hundreds of millions of the birds have been killed annually. Apart from a few slowly reproducing species which occur in low numbers or in a few large colonies, man has probably seldom made a long-term reduction in numbers of a bird.

It is clear that such a control system is not effective. However, there are times when numbers may be temporarily reduced and some advantage gained. The pigeon may do serious damage to spring greens or early crops of peas. Heavy shooting may reduce the damage locally, though probably more by scaring the birds away rather than by reducing their numbers greatly.

Temporary reductions in numbers can occasionally also be brought about by shooting after the end of the winter. At this point the level of the population is at its lowest and most birds that have survived the winter competition are likely to survive and breed. Removal of a bird at this time does reduce the breeding population for that year. Hunting in this way adds the mortality due to shooting on to the maximum losses due to nature. Shooting earlier merely changes the way in which the individual dies.

Indeed, some people believe that hunting early in the winter may result in larger numbers of breeding birds in the following spring. This could easily occur if there were more birds than can be supported by a fixed winter food supply. Removal of some birds at the beginning of the winter leaves food that they would have eaten for the others later, whereas if birds are not removed the stocks of food become scarcer sooner, so that there are greater losses from starvation towards the end.

I discussed earlier the reproductive rates of birds, and Wynne-Edwards's view that most species were breeding less rapidly than they could to prevent over-exploitation of the food supply. It is clear that such a theory is inapplicable to birds such as the pigeon, where shooting removes a large number of individuals but does not affect the level of the breeding population. When man starts to kill them in large numbers, there is no evidence that they increase their reproduction to compensate for the new source of mortality. Many birds die from competition for food during the winter. Such species must be over-producing and it is likely therefore that they are raising as many young as possible.

While almost all bird populations can make good their numbers from losses due to man, there is one way in which their numbers can be reduced drastically and permanently: by removal of the habitat. Once the area which contains the food for themselves and for raising young has been removed, the chances of a species recovering its numbers have gone for good. In the case of migrant species the position is more complex since, not only must the breeding habitat be retained, but also that on the wintering ground and even that in the areas where the migrants pause en route. Removal of the habitat may be direct, or it may be by poisoning such as with chlorinated hydrocarbons: in either case the area is unfit for the birds' existence.

It is by changes of the landscape that man has had his greatest effects on bird populations; the most marked effect has been on marshland birds by draining swamps for farming. Terrestrial birds, whether dwellers in woodland or in open country have, for the large part, adapted themselves to man's changes and even, in the case of some vegetarians such as the house sparrow and the wood pigeon, have benefited from man's use of the land. By a twist of fate, the species which man regards as pests cannot be eliminated by removal of their habitat since the habitat that needs to be removed is farmland.

It seems likely that birds will continue to live alongside man, though the species composition in an area may change considerably with changing land-use, as it has undoubtedly done in the past. The relatively high reproductive rates of most species enable them to recover quickly in numbers after any periods of losses and makes them difficult to control; certainly it is seldom economic to try.

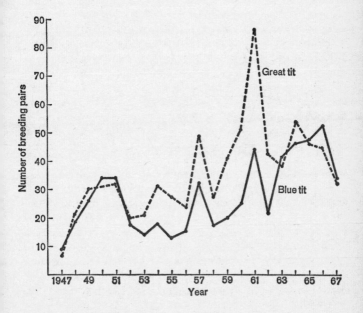

Figure 1. The number of breeding pairs of great tits and blue tits in Marley Wood near Oxford.

Bibliography

REFERENCES

Lack, D., *The Natural Regulation of Animal Numbers*, Oxford University Press, 1954. *Population Studies of Birds*, Oxford University Press, 1966.

Murton, R. K., *The Wood Pigeon*, New Naturalist, Collins, 1965.

Wynne-Edwards, V. C., *Animal Dispersion in Relation to Social Behaviour*, Oliver & Boyd, 1962.

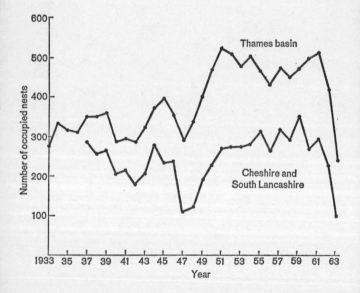

Figure 2.   The numbers of occupied nests of the heron in two different areas in England.
Particularly hard winters occurred in 1940, 1941, 1942, 1945 and 1947 and again in 1962 and 1963. Data from the British Trust for Ornithology's Heron Census, organized by J. Stafford.

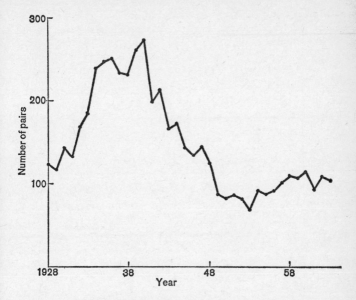

Figure 3. The numbers of pairs of white storks in Oldenburg, Germany. Graph drawn from data in Tantzen 1962.

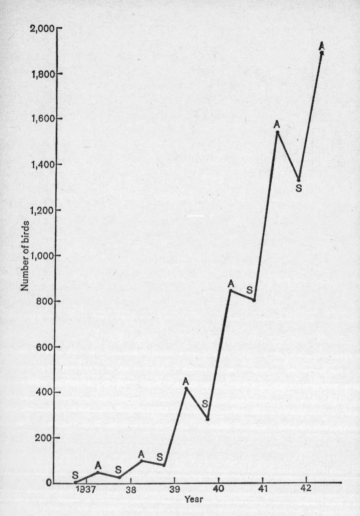

Figure 4. Number of pheasants on Protection Island, Washington State, after the initial introduction of two cocks and six hens in 1937. (The island was open to shooting and other disturbances from 1942 onwards). A = autumn count, S = spring count. Data from Einarsen 1945.

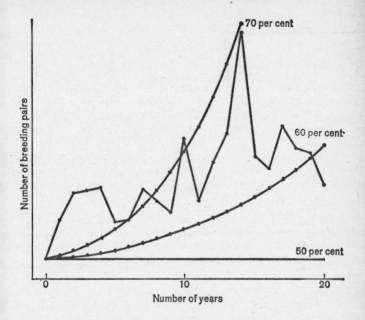

Figure 5. (a) Theoretical changes in number of small birds if only 10 per cent of the young survive, but 50, 60 or 70 per cent of the adult birds survive.

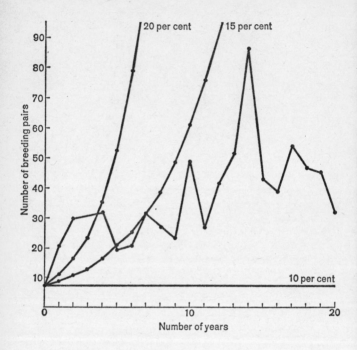

Figure 5. (b) Theoretical changes in numbers if only 50 per cent of the adult birds survive, but 10, 15 or 20 per cent of the young survive (assuming each pair has 10 young per year).

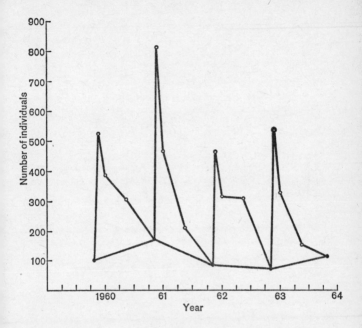

Figure 6. The changes in numbers within a year, based on the Oxford Study of Great Tits (see Figure 1). The line joining the solid circles is that representing the numbers of breeding adults from year to year. The three open circles for each year show, respectively, the total of adults plus eggs, the total of adults plus young that have left the nest, and the estimated autumn population.

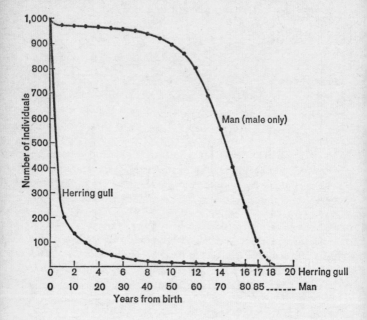

Figure 7. Survivorship curves for man and herring gull (note different scales of years for the two species). Both curves commence from 1,000 newborn young or eggs. Data for herring gull from Paynter 1966; for man (males only England and Wales for 1966) from the Registrar General's Statistical Review of England and Wales for 1966.

Population Control among Large Mammals

Leslie Brown

Large mammals, like small mammals, have to contend during their lives with several main factors militating against their survival. The most important and obvious of these are predation by the large carnivora (which may prey on each other as well as on herbivores), disease, and starvation. To survive in terms of evolutionary time it is necessary to be able to recover from the onslaught of any one of these factors, or in extreme circumstances, of all three together. It will not suffice to survive most of the time. At very long intervals a species may have to face the onslaught of some entirely new menace, such as the introduction into Africa of rinderpest in the last decade of the nineteenth century, or the Black Death in Europe. The fact that humans and animals alike survived, and recovered from these quite unprecedented onslaughts is a testimony of the ability of species to survive, even in conditions far more adverse than are met with in everyday life.

In recent years attention has also been focused on the possibility of other forms of population control, quite different in operation from those listed above, all of which involve a reduction in numbers by death, violent or unpleasant. It is likely that among some animal species there may be behavioural or reproductive patterns that work to limit the natural potential for increase (ordinarily necessary to recover from the effects of predation, disease or starvation) and which operate especially when the population is dense. This type of mechanism limiting population would tend to mitigate, or reduce the frequency of attacks of the indiscriminate killers, disease and starvation, and would act together with predation to maintain the population at a stable high level.

Of the three factors first mentioned predation has a continuing effect from day to day, and in undisturbed animal populations its effects are relatively slight. Predators take a regular toll of different ages, classes and species of animals, with very few exceptions. A few very large species, such as elephant, rhinoceros or hippopotamus, and to a lesser extent buffalo, gaur, and other large bovines, may largely or entirely escape predation, as may very fleet or elusive species that are not particularly common. Species that are unpalatable may also escape predation for a time, but they will be killed if more palatable species become rare or difficult to catch.

Regular natural day-to-day predation helps to keep populations in check, or in balance with their environment, but does not at any time result in a catastrophic or very rapid reduction in numbers. It is only when man comes upon the scene, with his proverbial incapacity to regulate his actions in accordance with environmental conditions, that any large species of mammal is actually endangered by predation. Within the last few centuries many large mammal species have either been extinguished altogether or else brought to the verge of extinction by man, and the tendency continues to the present day when there is little or no excuse for such ignorance. Some species thus rendered very rare by man, may have reached such a point of low numbers from which it is difficult for them to recover their former abundance. Most species, however, even when protected at the very last moment, such as the sea otter, or the black wildebeest, have shown impressive powers of recovery from excessive human predation.

Disease acts upon populations in a more indiscriminate and irregular manner. Some disease may be present at all times, but large-scale mortality occurs only during epizootics. Disease can attack those animals large enough to escape the worst effects of day to day predation. Thus buffalo in East Africa were in many areas nearly wiped out at the turn of the century by rinderpest, and were then less generally common than they are today. In

Africa hippopotami and especially kudu may die in considerable numbers from anthrax.

Attacks of disease may often, but not always, be density-dependent, occurring mainly when the population of a particular species is at a high level. The surviving reduced population may for years be quite free of the disease until the numbers have recovered, or until other adverse conditions facilitate the development of another attack. However, in the case of rinderpest, even small local populations of, for instance, greater kudu are repeatedly decimated by successive epizootics to near extinction, for instance on Marsabit Mountain.

In the course of many generations populations may acquire a resistance or immunity to disease characteristic of the environment. Thus the African antelopes and equines are in general immune or highly resistant to the diseases carried by the tsetse fly, while domestic bovines and equines, none of which have been in Africa for long, are not. Many African antelope species however, are not resistant to rinderpest, which entered Africa late in the nineteenth century with domestic stock and decimated many populations. Through natural selection many antelopes may in time develop resistance to rinderpest and domestic stock to trypanosomiasis. The Ndama cattle of Guinea have, for instance, developed a fair resistance to trypanosomiasis and do not succumb to the disease under severe challenge nearly as easily as do zebu. Such resistance may not be complete, but will mitigate the worst effects of an epizootic.

Starvation, as a decimating agent, acts only when for some reason or another the environment has become incapable of maintaining the whole population. Such conditions can be brought about by a severe winter, by drought, by human or other ill usage of the environment, or by other such factors. Starvation strikes mainly when the population is at a high level. It is obvious that a small population resulting for instance from an attack of disease will be able to find more to eat per individual than a large population could. For starvation to be effective as a decimating factor the food supply must usually be overstrained, when in extreme cases, the kill, of young and old alike, may be of catastrophic proportions. Sometimes, however, starvation can be caused, not by the amount but the quality of the food supply and then has a selective effect, as for instance when the protein content of the grassland in a drought is adequate to maintain adult females alive but does not permit them to produce milk for their calves; the latter then die and the females survive.

Starvation may be regarded as the ultimate of the three factors normally controlling populations. If predation or disease does not effect a reduction, a stage will be reached when starvation does. It is evident that behaviour patterns which may help a population to limit itself would be of the greatest value in relation to starvation, rather than to disease or predation. On predation they would have limited effect, and on disease, as far as is known, still less.

In any natural population all three of these factors act together. Predation helps to prevent the over-rapid increase of animals to a point where an epizootic disease could sweep through them with catastrophic effect, or where the environment would be incapable of supporting the population and starvation would take a heavy toll. Predators may not – in fact do not – confine their attention to diseased or weakened animals, but it is safe to say that such sick and weakly animals have a very poor chance of recovering or surviving in the presence of an active healthy population of powerful predators. During the attack of a disease, or starvation, the amount of carrion lying about may reduce, for the time being, the predatory effect of some carnivora, such as the hyena which, contrary to general belief, is an active predator on healthy antelope herds. Starvation, likewise, may so weaken animals that disease is able to get a hold and kill them in conditions when otherwise no epizootic might develop. The combined effect of all three factors, probably assisted by behaviour patterns, is to maintain the population in a relatively stable balance with the environment, which has a measurable and finite capacity to maintain populations of animals and which cannot consciously be improved or altered by any other animal but man. Catastrophic reductions in the populations of large mammals are as a whole less frequent and regular in natural conditions than in such small animals as the lemming.

After this general survey we may proceed to a more particular discussion of the various factors. Predation is a subject which has interested many biologists, and which is notoriously difficult to study. Predators themselves are invariably much less numerous, and usually much more difficult to observe than are their prey animals. It is often difficult to detect what may have happened to an individual which is missing from a herd of possible prey. The remains are seldom discovered, and, if they are, carrion feeders, such as hyenas, may have obliterated the traces of the original killer. Leopards are common, powerful, successful, ubiquitous, but exceedingly elusive animals; even in national parks, where they have become relatively tame in recent times, they are seldom observed killing. However, despite the difficulties, several good studies have been done in recent years on the effects of predation, in particular on the tiger, lion, wild dog, and hyena in Asia and Africa, and the puma and wolves in North America.

The effect of predation may vary from a slight to a major limiting effect. In the case of the tiger in India, studied by Schaller in Kanha National Park, predation was judged to be the major factor limiting the growth of populations of deer in the park, while in the case of one deer species, the swamp deer or bara-singha, predation by tigers was considered to be the major factor preventing a small population with poor annual recruitment from recovering its numbers. This study may not be entirely typical, as it was carried out over 14 months only in a small area beleaguered by excessive human use all round, so that the effect of predation might locally have been exaggerated. However, the area had advantages lacking in many predator-prey studies, in that the tiger was the only regular predator in the area on several species. The quantitative effect of the carnivora could therefore be more accurately estimated.

This study illustrated clearly one feature of predation – the selective effect of one species of predator upon a mixed population of the prey. The animals killed by the tiger included the very large and powerful gaur, several species of deer (chital, sambar and barasingha) and domestic stock (buffalo and cattle). The tiger was considered to be the only important predator, hyenas and leopards being rare. The food requirement of the tiger is about 12–15 lb. per day for an adult, and a proportion of each kill is necessarily inedible or wasted. On this basis it could be calculated that an adult tiger has to kill 6,250–7,820 lb. of prey per annum to survive, and that the population of tigers in Kanha Park would kill 41,000–55,000 lb. of meat each year. This figure corresponds well with the 50,600 lb. of wild and domestic animals killed by all predators in the Kanha area, of which 6,800 lb. was domestic stock and 43,800 lb. wild animals.

Of the latter figure, 16,375 lb. was composed of chital, and 14,100 lbs. of gaur. However, the chital losses to predators (mostly tigers) were 115 young and 85 adults, while those of the gaur were only 25 young and 7 adults. Thus, although about a third by weight of the tiger's wild food came from gaur, the effect on the total adult population of this species was much more slight than that on the chital. The barasingha, a deer about twice the size of a chital, and perhaps of an optimum size for a tiger to kill, provided 9,450 lb. of kills to tigers from a total population of 82 animals (falling to 55 a year later), whereas the chital provided rather less than twice this amount of food (16,375 lb.) from a total population of 900–1,000, more than ten times that of barasingha. It seemed clear that in this case predation by tigers – combined with and aggravated by poaching and disease – could cause eventual extinction of this small population of barasingha.

In East Africa, on the plains of the Serengeti and in other places, there is a much wider variety both of predators and of ungulates than in India. Of the herbivores which occur, one (the elephant) is so large as to be for practical purposes immune to predation by lions, the largest of the predators. Rhinoceros and hippopotamus, large though they are, are sometimes killed by lions, especially when young or, as in the Luangwa valley, where overgrazing near the river forces hippopotami to graze far inland, so that they are at a disadvantage with lions. In such cases the lions maul their prey to death rather than kill them outright.

All other herbivores, including the large and powerful buffalo, (which is a staple food of lions in some areas) are subject to regular predation. The predators, in order of size and individual strength are the lion, leopard, spotted hyena, cheetah, striped hyena, wild dog, serval cat, caracal, and several species of jackals, smaller wild cats and mongooses. There is an overlap, not only in the size of animal killed by these various predators, but in the method used for killing. Lions for instance may be obliged to kill a wildebeest by stealth from reasonably good cover but wild dogs or hyenas can kill the same animal by running it down in completely open short grass country or bare soil where a lion could not approach it. Cheetahs kill Thomson's gazelle by speed in the open, lions by stalking them to close range. Hyenas, which can run at 40 m.p.h. by night, are then easily able to catch adult zebra which by day could escape but at night can only run at 25 m.p.h.

The quantitative effect of a mixed population of predators upon their prey has not yet been fully worked out, and much work in progress is still not published. In the course of these studies many long-accepted notions have been exploded. For instance it has been found that hyenas are among the most active predators upon such large ungulates as wildebeest, and that lions frequently do not kill for themselves but depend upon kills taken from hyenas (described, incidentally, as parasitism whereas it is clearly piracy). However, it seems likely that although no single species of predator would have a sufficient controlling effect upon the commoner prey animals, the combined effect of several species, acting upon young and adults selectively, would be much more marked.

Take the case of the Ngorongoro crater, a famous wildlife spectacle in North Tanzania. It is estimated that this caldera of 102 square miles contains a rather regular resident population of about 25,000–30,000 antelopes and zebra, including 15,000 wildebeest. There are, in Ngorongoro, at the present time, about 60 lions, whose annual kill (working on a similar estimate to that of Schaller for the somewhat larger and perhaps more voracious tiger) might be about 210,000 lb. The commonest species killed by lions in Ngorongoro are zebra, wildebeest and hartebeest. The total amount required annually by the Ngorongoro lions could, for instance, theoretically be provided by 100 zebra, 300 wildebeest and 100 hartebeest. This is about 1·7 per cent of the combined population of these species, from which it is clear that lions alone could not prevent these species from increasing.

However, when the effect of lions is considered in conjunction with that of hyenas, cheetahs and wild dogs, the other predators which might kill these herbivores, the combined effect upon the population is much more serious. There are approximately 420 spotted hyenas in the Ngorongoro crater, made up of groups, or clans, of 10 to 100 animals each. They probably kill about 1,500–2,000 large herbivores a year, mainly wildebeest and zebra, but including some gazelles. These kills are drawn from young or adolescents of the species concerned, though adults are also taken, especially at night; lions sometimes appropriate hyenas' kills. Cheetahs concentrate upon gazelles, but several adults working together can kill an adult wildebeest or hartebeest. Wild dogs, which are exceedingly efficient predators, killing almost 100 per cent of what they pursue, again concentrate on gazelles, but obtain 21 per cent of their food from juvenile wildebeest. The combined effect of lions, hyenas and wild dogs on the wildebeest population may be computed at about 10 per cent of the total numbers, the lions killing chiefly adults, the others young as well as adults.

In the Serengeti plains, an area similar ecologically to Ngorongoro, and populated by the same animals, the predation situation is different. The main population of herbivores, wildebeest, zebra and others, is here migratory whereas the lions are resident in woodland territories. When the herbivores migrate to the open plains few lions follow them, so that wildebeest and zebra escape the worst effects of lion predation. Individuals may die on the plains of old age, which would be virtually impossible in Ngorongoro. When the herbivores are on the plains the lions themselves must subsist on resident herbivores such as buffalo. The total population of lions is not, therefore, directly related to the total biomass of potential prey, but to that part of it which is left when the great herds have migrated into the open plains.

The effect of even a combined population of predators, however, must in the long run be inadequate to prevent increase of the population of the prey. If predation were effectively to account for the natural annual increase there would be no 'surplus' to be taken by disease, which would inevitably strike sooner or later. If a species is to survive, predation alone cannot be allowed to limit prey populations.

It is possible that disease and predation are inter-related. Recent research in East Africa has shown that wild animals suffer from a number of diseases. In the Nairobi Park, for instance, 8 out of 26 antelopes were found to be suffering from muscular dystrophy, 9 out of 26 from parasitic bronchitis and 3 out of 26 from both. Muscular dystrophy, in particular, could be expected to place a suffering animal at a severe disadvantage when it attempted to escape a predator. The fact that at normal times a population of wild animals appears to contain very few individuals that look sick may not only be a reflection upon their superior resistance to locally common diseases but an indication that any sick animals are usually soon eliminated by predators. However, this remains to be fully proved, and of course it cuts both ways. Predators also suffer from disease, so that they cannot catch their prey. In the same study infectious feline enteritis, Nairobi bleeding disease, and spirocercosis were found in carnivora examined, which included leopard, cheetah and wild cats.

Predation is also related to territorial behaviour, not only of the predator, but also of the prey. Among the Ngorongoro wild dogs, for instance, 53 per cent of kills were Thomson's gazelle, and of these 60 per cent were adult territorial males, which are the last age class to flee from danger. The removal of these territorial males may have enabled younger animals to fill otherwise unattainable niches in the social hierarchy of the species. Likewise, single territorial males of hartebeest, wildebeest and topi are frequently selected in preference to animals in herds by lions. Any human hunter knows that the 'old solitary male' not only carries the best trophy but also is easier to approach than a male in his prime protected by a large herd of alert females.

Disease as a killer of large wild animals in the wild state is even less clearly observed than predation. Often the only signs of an epizootic are putrefying carcasses in thick cover. The quantitative effects are often very difficult to measure directly, but can sometimes be inferred by counts before and after the attack. Talbot (1963) found that 'yearling disease' (rinderpest accounted for 80 per cent of wildebeest calves surviving to seven months old; the mortality was associated with scouring on new grass following rain after drought, and is apparently not an annual occurrence. On Marsabit in 1960 a healthy population of greater kudu, perhaps totalling 300, was reduced to small groups totalling perhaps 50 by rinderpest. Kudu, in fact, seem particularly susceptible to several diseases. In Kruger Park in 1961, 1,054 carcasses enumerated after an anthrax outbreak included 771 greater kudu, about 15 per cent of the total estimated population. This may be compared with 75 waterbuck and 58 buffalo, the latter from a population of 9,500–10,500. Although, in this case, the effect of disease on buffalo was slight, the effects of rinderpest on this species at the end of the last century, while never accurately quantified, were generally admitted to be catastrophic. Foot and mouth disease also takes its toll, for instance, of giraffe in several areas of Kenya.

As stated earlier, disease and predation may interact. It will be evident that, in such a situation as the Ngorongoro crater, where hyenas may account for about 1,500–2,000 animals a year, if a severe attack of disease were to strike it would not then be necessary for the hyenas to kill these animals; food could be obtained without effort. Much the same applies in the case of starvation. If large scale deaths occur as a result of starvation the pressure on the survivors from predators such as hyenas will be reduced at first, though once the available supply of carrion rots or is eaten it will be sharply increased. Even such animals as the leopard have been known to acquire a taste for human flesh during epidemics when burial or cremation facilities are inadequate to cope with the mortality; later such animals may become predators on human beings for choice. This may affect different predators in different ways. The puma, for instance, appears only to eat what it itself kills, very seldom touching any carrion; in this case disease or starvation reducing a herd of deer in America would have the effect of increasing the predation pressure by pumas on the surviving population.

The puma has been estimated to take only about 2 per cent of the deer population in parts of America, but it has also been shown that even if the animals are not killed by pumas other environmental factors, mainly shortage of food, in the end reduce the population to the same level. The effects of malnutrition or starvation can often be observed in the absence of predation or disease, and have been well documented both for wild and domestic animals. For instance, in the case of the jawbone deer herd of California, studied for 3 years, winter mortality of deer varied from 5–33 per cent, averaging about 20 per cent. The effect was selective, culling the old and the young animals, while those in their prime survived. The total annual productivity of this particular herd was estimated at 33 per cent, while predation, largely in the form of human hunting, accounted for only about 7–8 per cent annually. In the circumstances, large-scale mortality from starvation in a severe winter was inevitable. The same can be observed in Britain in red deer, or hill sheep.

In New Zealand, where large animals such as red deer, chamois and others have all been introduced within the past century in the complete absence of any predatory animal or bird large enough to kill even the young, the population typically goes through an eruptive cycle, rising to a peak, then dying off on a catastrophic scale, with relatively minor fluctuations thereafter. Red deer were introduced to the Lake Marsh area of New Zealand in small numbers in 1901–4. By 1920–25 the population had reached a peak, from which it sharply declined. By 1934 deer were relatively scarce, but by 1937–8 numbers had built up again. The actual peak in the population probably occurred 37–42 years after the first introduction, in a population not affected by human or any other predation till 1953–7. In 1958, when this population was studied, the environment had been severely damaged, and most of the deer present were in poor condition, so that further reduction could be anticipated.

A classic case of this type of catastrophic loss following an eruptive cycle occurred in the Kajiado district of Masailand in Kenya in 1961-2. Following upon the universal enforcement of rinderpest control measures, coupled with other veterinary benefits, and in the absence of severe predation by carnivora or an adequate take-off for sale by human beings, the population of cattle rose from an estimated 300,000 in 1946 to about 720,000 in 1961. This population was in excess of the carrying capacity of the environment, which was severely damaged by overgrazing. In 1961 a severe drought (which killed many wild animals also) followed by record rainfall and catastrophic floods reduced the cattle population by 65 per cent, to an estimated 220,000 in 1962.

The capital loss, even at a relatively low price per head, was of the order of £4,000,000 to £5,000,000, while it became necessary for the government to provide famine relief for the Masai to the value of at least another £1,000,000. Herds are again increasing and, less than a decade later, the grassland, which recovered spectacularly, is again in places showing signs of strain.

Starvation is probably the most important killer in all populations of large animals. Predation, as we have seen, may have a relatively slight or a considerable effect, according to circumstances, and disease may also take a toll. However, if a population of animals, as in the case of the Masai cattle (and the same applies to many other situations of the type) is artificially protected from disease or predation or both, it is inevitable that starvation will kill off the surplus at long or short intervals. In climates with a cold winter this effect may be annually observed to a greater or lesser degree; and in tropical climates it may be observed at longer intervals, corresponding usually with severe drought years which may occur in regular climatic cycles. In such cases the population builds up over a period of good years, to drop catastrophically in the drought. In all cases these effects of starvation could be mitigated by allowing the natural effect of predation by carnivora to take its full toll, by increased human hunting of certain species such as red deer which are excessively numerous in biologically artificial situations, and, in the case of domestic stock, by ensuring that herds are not allowed to build up to numbers in excess of the carrying capacity of the environment.

It remains to consider certain rather peculiar or unusual cases of population control. We may first consider the case of certain animals which are so large and powerful that they naturally escape predation, and can therefore only be controlled by disease, starvation, or some other regulatory mechanism. Animals of this type might for instance, include the sperm whale, the elephant (Indian or African) and perhaps the white rhinoceros. Of the last only 20 were thought to be alive in the Umfolozi Game Reserve in Natal in 1920, an area of 72,000 acres. They had increased to 120 in 1929, 500 in 1953, 567 in 1959 and over 700 in the early sixties, a mean rate of about 85 per cent of the original population per annum. In the last few years many have been translocated to other places in their former range, as they were rapidly outstripping the capacity of their limited environment to support them. In Umfolozi they do not suffer from predation because there are no lions; but in the Kruger Park the rhinos have demonstrated, by the ease with which they repel the lions, that their increase would have occurred almost or quite as fast in the presence of predators.

African elephants are not regularly attacked by predators at any stage of their lives. The calves remain close to the females, and by the time a young bull shows any sign of independence (at about 10 years old) he is already too big to be attacked by lions. In several African National Parks a spectacular recent increase in the elephant population has caused widespread changes in the environment, bush and trees being replaced by grass. The situation appears to be one in which one could expect a catastrophic population crash, but in the elephant this does not seem to occur. Rather a series of factors gradually reduces the recruitment rate of the herds over a period of many years, so that in the end the population declines again. Some such effect might, indeed, be expected to have evolved in a very large animal immune from the attacks of any known predators. The question is not so much whether the elephant populations will decline, but whether, when they have declined, the environment itself will return to its former state or will be permanently altered.

In two elephant populations in the Murchison Falls Park and one in Tsavo it has appeared that the recruitment rate of herds is reduced by a combination of increased age at puberty, increased calving interval and increased calf mortality. The age at puberty in Tsavo (of healthy population) is $12\frac{1}{2}$ for females and $14\frac{1}{2}$ for males; in Murchison North Bank (rather overpopulated) 14, and 15; in Murchison South Bank (very overpopulated) 18 and $19\frac{1}{2}$. Likewise the mean calving interval in Tsavo is about 6·8 years and in Murchison 8·9 years; a female in Tsavo may produce, say, 8–10 calves in her lifetime, in Murchison 4–5.

Recruitment rate is also reduced by increased calf mortality in Murchison. This is not (as for instance is the case with wildebeest in a drought year) brought about by actual shortage of milk. Elephants continue to lactate for several years and a calf may be fed by adults other than its dam. Heat stress is one likely cause, and another is the absence of suitable browse for the young animal. A third may be an indirect effect of poor nutrition of the adults, resulting in a disadvantageous calving rhythm.

In the North Bank population the females calve mainly from December–March, in the dry season; on the South Bank from April–July, in the wet season. The effect is that since the greatest stress on maternal reserves does not arise until some months after calving, the females on the North Bank suffer this stress at a favourable time in the wet season and those on the South Bank at an unfavourable time, in the dry season. The factor initiating this effect appears to be the low nutritional plane of the females on the South Bank, which retards the date at which they are able to conceive. While those on the North Bank are well nourished, and able to conceive in April–May, those on the South Bank have to feed throughout most of the wet season to be able to conceive in August–October. This results, apparently, in the disadvantageous calving time on the South Bank. Similar effects have been observed in other animals. For instance, in the white-tailed deer it has been shown that ovulation is dependent on the plane of nutrition.

Knowledge of such subtle effects on population control is only in its infancy, and it is also only within the last two decades that the probably important effect of territorial behaviour has been grasped, let alone understood. It has been recognized for a long time that carnivora maintain territories by scent marking, urinating at particular places, etc., but it is only rather recently that it has been recognized that herbivores also maintain territories. Thomson's gazelle, for instance, mark their territories by delicately inserting the end of a grass stem into the orbital glands, leaving a small blackish bead of dried material on the stem. The 'solitary male' hartebeest, wildebeest or topi seen dotted about on open plains are in fact males in possession of and defending a territory, where they will be visited by breeding herds of females; they are not past breeding, but are the most active breeding males in the population.

The most striking territorial displays are performed by the Uganda kob. In this species males collect on well-known display grounds, where they remain and are sought by females. This behaviour seems to be density dependent in that it is found only where populations of kob are large, as in the Semliki Valley. Where the population is less dense individual males maintain single, well-spaced territories. A communal display ground with 12–15 active males is used year after year, and is ecologically altered, with a centre of short annual grasses where it has been overgrazed. It appears that in areas where communal display grounds occur breeding is maximized; in such areas all females examined had either given birth recently or were pregnant. In contrast, in areas where single males maintained individual territories copulations were often unsuccessful or abnormal, and breeding rate and survival perhaps lower. This might be a case where a high population is necessary to initiate the social behaviour leading to successful breeding patterns.

The larger carnivora are commonly assumed to be density dependent upon the numbers of possible prey. It is doubtful if this is really so, and in the Serengeti, as we have seen, it is not so. Until the full quantitative effect of a mixed population of large predators has been more or less accurately computed it is impossible to be definite, but lions, for instance, are strongly territorial. More than a certain number, irrespective of the abundance of food supply, cannot exist in the same area, and much interterritorial demonstration, fighting and even cannibalism occurs. The home range in a well stocked area such as Serengeti or Ngorongoro may contain far more prey than the predators can possibly utilize, but in some other areas not so well-stocked, such as the Etosha Pan Game Reserve, the number of lions in a given area may be as great and the pressure exerted by them on the prey consequently more severe. In this case the predator is ensuring, by maintaining a much larger home range than it really needs, that the likelihood of a population crash on the part of the predators, as a result of, for example, severe drought reducing the ungulate population, is remote.

It will be evident from the foregoing that the factors controlling the numbers of large animals, both among herbivora and carnivora, are exceedingly complex and in need of much more study before anything like a complete picture in most situations can emerge. Virtually every situation, moreover, as demonstrated by the difference between the effect of predation on the Serengeti and in Ngorongoro, must be examined individually, though similar features will naturally apply over wide areas. However, nothing that has been discovered to date invalidates the general views expressed here to the effect that, as a rule, predation is of relatively minor importance as a control factor when compared to the effects of epizootic disease or starvation. Nor can an unlimited population of animals, wild or tame, exist indefinitely in any given finite area. A time comes when it will be catastrophically decimated by starvation if not by disease or – as apparently is the case with elephants – will gradually decline as a result of deterioration of the habitat. Even in the carefully maintained absence of predation and disease, starvation will inevitably kill sooner or later. There is certainly a lesson to be learned here for the world's commonest large mammal, man.

Bibliography

REFERENCES

Kruuk, H., 'Clan System and Feeding Habits of Spotted Hyenas (*crocuta crocuta erxleben*)', *Nature*, 1966.

Laws, R. M., and Parker, I. S. C., *Recent Studies on Elephant Populations in East Africa*,

Leopold, A. S. *et al.*, 'The Jawbone Deer Herd', Game Bulletin No. 4, Museum of Vertebrate Zoology, University of California, 1961.

Leuthold, W., 'Variations in Territorial Behaviour of Uganda Kob *Adenota kop thomasi* (Neumann 1898)', *Behaviour*, 1966, XXVII, pp. 214–57.

Riney, T., *et al.*, 'The Lake Monk Expedition: an Ecological Study in South Fjordland', Bulletin 135, Department of Scientific and Industrial Research, New Zealand, 1959.

Riney, T., 'The Impact of Introductions of Large Herbivores on the Tropical Environment', Proceedings of the Ninth Tech. Meeting, Nairobi, Part 3, pp. 261–73, 1963.

Robinette, W. L., Gaswiler, J. S., and Morris, O. W., 'Food Habits of the Cougar in Utah and Nevada', *Journal of Wildlife Management*, 23, (3), pp. 261–72, 1959.

Schaller, G., *The Deer and the Tiger*, Chicago University Press, 1967.

Schaller, G., 'Serengeti Lion Study', Bulletin of the U.N.E.S.C.O., Regional Centre for Science and Technology, III, (1), pp. 43–5, 1968.

Talbot, L. M. and M., 'Wildebeest Ecology and Population', Wildlife Monographs, 1963.

Wynne-Edwards, V. C., *Animal Dispersion in Relation to Social Behaviour*, Oliver & Boyd, 1962.

Population

John B. Calhoun

Recently I. A. Richards, out of his experience as poet and semanticist, has introduced the idea of 'feedforward' as a concept embodying all those strategies of action and thought whereby we attempt to predict the consequences of our next direction into the future. He holds that in some rudimentary form we customarily utilize feedforward during each phase of our day-to-day lives. As a very simple case we may go down a flight of stairs in the dark, and having prejudged the flight to consist of seven steps we set our body position and the foot going forward while on the sixth step in anticipation of there being a seventh step. But in fact there might have been only six steps, and as a consequence we stumble upon arriving at the floor too soon. Although this error may be utilized in later actions as feedback to assure our safe passage down this particular stair, the point Richards makes is that we were making certain predictions about the future, even though they were in error. Richards further points out that the value of feedforward lies not in determining the exact course of the future over some long course of many decision points, but rather in guiding our path on the basis of re-evaluating our expectations as we proceed. To do this we must have some set of relevant values, variables or concepts upon which to base our modified expectations. In this connexion writing poetry and any actions we may take in guiding the development of populations have much in common. It is improbable that any truly creative poem would emerge from an engineered outline which dictated the sequence of content from beginning to end before writing. In like fashion there can probably be no creative population – one which adjusts to the present while preserving considerable diversity of options for the future – where its course over a long period of time is rigidly programmed.

Both art and science have their roles to play in any decisions which govern the course of populations. Note my use of the term 'decision'. We are reaching the stage in the evolution of the planet Earth where the future of the population of man himself, as well as those of the plants and animals which share the globe with him, will in large measure be determined by decisions that we as members of the human species make. Science can provide an understanding of processes which affect the growth, persistence and characteristics of a population. Each of these kinds of understanding has generally been gained from a concentration upon only a few of the many variables that may affect a population, and in most cases in experimental studies by excluding the opportunity for many potential variables to function. From the present base of scientific knowledge we cannot predict anywhere near completely what will be the full impact on any population of the simultaneous function of many variables which have previously been studied in relative isolation. And yet the pressure of ecological, social and political events necessitate that decisions about the future of populations must be taken. At this point we become involved in the art of making value-judgements which utilize the best available insights from science. A small sample of representative literature most closely based on the 'hard facts' from science is given at the end of this paper. However, beyond these hard facts the scientist has a role to play in presenting his interpretation of the implications of his insights and even in suggesting the possible consequences of the operation of variables which remain inadequately studied. This is a borderline role which scientists have generally avoided. But the threats to real populations can no longer await full scientific elucidation; the scientist must participate insofar as he is able in the process by which value-judgements about populations are made. I shall here try to play this non-scientific role of a scientist to show how he is in a position to recognize conditions and processes, the existence and possible consequences of which have hardly entered the public domain of awareness.

As an example let me cite a 'happening' that recently influenced the initiation of a large scale experimental research programme on the growth of populations of house mice in my own laboratory. In 1962 Dr Alexander Kessler and I began a correspondence about a research programme he was designing to analyse the influence of population growth on the survival of animals with differing genetic backgrounds. From my experience with the study of rodents in artificially structured habitats he wished to know my recommendation for a habitat that might be suitable for his study. It so happened that I had just completed a formulation of a habitat that, with appropriate modifications of size and content to fit the kind of animal, could be used for such diverse animals as mice and chickens. I thought that this habitat would be ideal for a total population of between 12 and 50 adults with the investigator functioning as a predator, reducing any increase above this range so that he could study the social relations among the individuals within a closed population or social group. For house mice this habitat would have a diameter of about 10 feet. At this point of conveying to Dr Kessler my ideas about habitat construction our correspondence was fortunately interrupted. I did not hear from him again until his study was nearly completed and he invited me to visit his laboratory. The space that he had available for housing his experimental habitats was limited to a single laboratory room in the Rockefeller Institute. Further, he wished to study at least two populations. He therefore reduced the habitat down to about 5 feet in diameter rather than 10 feet as I had suggested. In addition he had initiated his breeding population in each habitat with 32 adults. This latter was necessitated by the fact that he wished to start off with 4 inbred strains and judged 4 pairs of each to be the minimum that could be tolerated to try to reduce random gene drift, a loss of hereditary material by chance rather than as a consequence of selection to tolerate increased density.

When Dr Kessler showed me the resultant populations just before he terminated the study, one contained over 800 adults and weaned mice and the other over 1,000. In the latter case there was less than three square inches per mouse – standing room only! No other experimental study of population growth of rodents known to me had attained such density. Typically the density in comparable space had levelled off at one tenth that in Kessler's study. The origin of this tenfold difference remains unexplained – that is, by existing experiments. However, insights drawn from several sources begin to suggest what may have happened. I wish to make clear that the trend of thought I am now developing is one that the scientist often engages in but normally does not make public until several years later after the conclusion of studies generated by such speculations.

Most scientists who have so far engaged in experimental studies of animal populations have a strong grounding in ecology. They know that after an area has been depopulated as a consequence of some biological or physical catastrophe the population begins to reconstitute itself from a few survivors or invaders. Thus in the experimental model it has been usual to initiate a population with a very few individuals, rarely more than 1–4 pairs. Most initial litters survive and many members of these contribute progeny to the growing population. However, from the early history of the population, strife characterizes some of the relations among adults and this strife becomes accentuated as the density of adults increases. As a consequence, mortality of adults and young increases, the adequacy of maternal care declines, and even the conception rate decreases. Finally in experimental habitats of about the size of Kessler's, mortality balances natality and an upper limit of the order of 50 to 150 weaned animals prevails.

There appeared to be only one important variable between Kessler's study and those of most other investigators; he started his study with a far larger number of colonizers. This leads to the hypothesis that the larger the number of colonizing individuals the larger the ultimate size of the population before stress from increased density leads mortality and natality to come into balance. For this to be true it means that when two populations have each reached 100 adults, the members of the one initiated with sixteen pairs will be experiencing much less stress from social interaction than the one started with only two pairs. This difference must then be traced back to the social relationships among the colonizers, particularly as these involve aggression. In the literature on aggression one conclusion stands out. An individual tends to exhibit aggressive actions towards associates to the extent that he has resided alone in a particular place in its range. In essence the individual by being alone in particular locations develops an identification with the spatial content and configurations of his immediate environs. They become part of him; his ego has a spatial radius defining a personal space which moves about with the animal like a circle with the individual at the centre. Any encroachment into this personal space elicits aggressive action. In animals with dispersed homes two individuals can approach each other rather closely at locations half way between their respective homes with much reduced likelihood of aggression because their respective personal spaces decline with increasing distance from their home sites.

We may apply this formulation to the colonizers of experimental habitats. All these habitats have been so restricted that any inhabitant can within a very few minutes traverse its entire configuration. Under these circumstances, whenever two individuals are active at the same time, each will interfere with the other's opportunity to develop an identity with his environment. And since each individual on the average spends one fourth of his time active and roaming about through the habitat, any increase in number of individuals will increase the likelihood of interference with any individual developing a personal space into which he will defend encroachments by aggressive actions. Where a population is initiated by one or two pairs each member has the opportunity to incorporate portions of the physical surroundings into his own personal space. Territories in time or space become established and later-born individuals must frequently withdraw back into available shelters to avoid the aggression of the dominant or territorial individuals who defend encroachment upon their personal space. At the death or senescence of these more aggressive individuals some younger member, which had not yet withdrawn so extensively either psychologically or physically as a consequence of the actions of their dominant associates, will assume this vacated role. In this way there develops a social pattern of replacement of aggressive individuals which preserves and accentuates the degree of stress to the extent that the closed population without any opportunity for emigration will relatively soon attain a state where mortality balances natality. The several experimental populations of mice and rats I have studied conform to this interpretation.

Where the population starts its growth from a base of a large number of colonizers, no single individual will often be in any place without the presence of associates. Little exclusive identification with any portions of the physical environment can be made. Thus the radius of the personal space from the very beginning for all individuals is very short. This reduces the likelihood that any particular individual's personal space will be encroached upon unless physical contact occurs, and as a consequence little aggression will be elicited. Marked reduction of aggression inhibits the origin of that chain of endocrinological and behavioural changes which increase mortality, inhibit conception and disrupt maternal behaviour. A self-reinforcing social pattern becomes established in which personal space becomes ever more limited to the point that, even though the physical space per animal is reduced nearly to that required for each to lie down in, very little crowding exists because personal space has become reduced to the boundaries of the individual's skin; the world about no longer exists; each individual remains isolated in the confines of the capsule of its own skin despite the physical proximity of many others. Obviously this formulation is an overstatement of the case. In Kessler's study some aggression did remain even at its termination, and sufficient meaningful relations persisted to produce continued conceptions. However, the normal pattern of relationship between pup and mother no longer continued. Pups were scattered across the surface of the habitat to the extent that wherever a lactating female stopped there was a good chance that a pup would be close enough to work itself over and grasp a teat. Despite pup mortality enough survived through this random association to maintain population growth.

I have dwelt at some length on this one study for several

reasons. It shows that a whole new area of research can be opened up by someone like Dr Kessler who, from his medical, biochemical and genetic background of training, lacked some of the biases held by the ecologists who have been the primary ones previously involved in experimental studies of mammalian populations. And because of this lack of bias he initiated populations with a large number of colonizers. We have been so impressed with the possible validity of the interpretations suggested by this study that we have initiated a large-scale study in our laboratory varying both the size of the habitat and the number of colonizers.

In the end we can justify our experimental studies of animal populations only on the ground that insights from them will assist us in guiding the destinies of populations in more natural situations, whether they be of other animals or of man himself. We are approaching a unique and critical phase of human population growth and organization. The threat of overpopulation stands second only to that of nuclear warfare; either can destroy the course of human progress. Within the past few years there has grown up a 'scare' gambit in much of the writing on human populations. Beyond the overcrowding that will often likely arise before the world population growth can be terminated, one sees over and over again extrapolations to the not too distant future when there will be standing room only, one square yard per person if the present rate of population increase continues. Then as often as not there will follow qualifying statements that man has certain needs, space being one of them, which as limiting factors will induce man to curtail further increase in his numbers before the point of standing room only arrives. For a long time I have worried about whether there is any real basis for this hope. The implications of Kessler's study suggests that for all practical purposes, to where only food and shelter are limiting variables, man can go to 'standing room only'.

I am reminded of the story told about one of our famous American frontiersmen, Daniel Boone. As soon as a neighbour settled within 40 miles he felt crowded, pulled up stakes, and moved farther on to some place with less infringement on him.

That is an evaluation of personal space no one any longer maintains. In fact most of us can measure a significant reduction in our personal space within the past ten years. I think that there is no question that we can greatly reduce further our requirements for personal space. So far I have spoken of physical space. However, as a theoretical construct at least, conceptual space is interchangeable with physical space. The breadth of our insights and concerns in the arts, humanities, sciences and on the political and social scene can compensate for reductions in the physical parameters of our personal space. But just as surely as the need for physical space can be lost, or never gained, so can there arise a general deprivation in conceptual space. In fact there is a good reason to suspect that every reduction in the spatial aspects of personal space will be accompanied by an equal reduction in the conceptual aspects of personal space unless studied efforts are made to provide the means for increasing the extent of realization of human potentialities in the conceptual sphere. There is no logical reason why the human population could not trap itself into a situation where both the physical and conceptual parameters of personal space were to become reduced to the bare minimum of its present extent for the majority of the population.

Any discussion of population brings one face to face with the topic of crowding. At its simplest level crowding is synonymous with density. We speak of crowding more apples into a box or more people into a car. For apples this may be very well, but even here too many apples in a container can lead to crushing and opening up avenues for invasion of decay-generating fungi or bacteria. And take the situation of people in a car. Few of you have failed to observe two lovers driving along with the boy at the wheel and the girl so close to him as to nearly be sitting on his lap. One can hardly speak of them as being crowded, but each of you can readily select from your experience two individuals who even at the extreme opposite sides of the front seat of an automobile would feel crowded – they would feel uncomfortable in each other's presence if not outright verbally or physically antagonistic. In this latter instance there would be too much overlap of both physical and conceptual space. Crowding thus must also be assessed on the basis of degree of harmony among the held values of the individuals who are sufficiently spatially contiguous to be aware of each other's presence.

Let me take an example from domesticated breeds of rats to illustrate the universality of conflict in values, of overlapping and disharmonious conceptual space, as an aspect of crowding. This is a case where sixteen rats in a particular space and in a particular situation were not crowded, but the adding of a single additional individual produced an intensely crowded situation. This group of sixteen rats lived in a relatively spatially confined area containing a task situation requiring cooperation. At one place in their habitat I placed a water reservoir. The front face of the reservoir contained two levers, and a partition which the rats could easily see through separated the two levers. When a rat pressed a lever it might or might not result in a drop of water being delivered in a small cup. A treadle activating a microswitch covered the space in front of each lever. By appropriate circuitry the condition could be established which required that a rat be present in front of each lever for the levers to be unlocked so that the pressing of either would result in the delivery of water. The sixteen rats in this situation rapidly learned this task. Whenever one rat became thirsty it would go over to the access door in front of one of the two channels leading to a lever. Very shortly one of his companions would note his action and come over and stand beside him. Then they would enter simultaneously and begin drinking. In essence they had developed a value system involving collaborative effort and altruism. In the adjoining habitat, separated by a fence topped by an electrified wire there resided another group of 16 rats for whom I placed the opposite task. A rat could only get water if it entered the drinking situation alone; that is to say no rat could be on the treadle before the lever on the other side. These rats essentially learned to avoid each other. They did this fairly adequately. The only trouble was that since only one rat could drink at a time and each rat spent three-fourths of its time sleeping these disoperative rats, as I termed them, often experienced some difficulty in getting enough water. One of these disoperative rats learned how to jump over the barrier fence separating it from its cooperating neighbours. Whenever he would enter a channel leading to a water lever one of his cooperative companions would come over and join him. Although this action did unlock the lever before this disoperative rat, he nevertheless viewed this companion as behaving improperly according to the value system he had acquired in his former home. He would then back out of his channel, grasp the 'offending' companion by the tail, rear skin, or hind feet and pull him out. These cooperative animals, like the apples, became quite bruised as a consequence of one more being added to their number. In fact eight shortly died, and I had to anaesthetize the remainder to put them out of their misery. We are now beginning an extensive experimental programme on this topic of value conflict in rats and its resolution when one attempts to integrate two groups with opposite value systems. This aspect of crowding is certainly as important as that contributed by density alone.

Competition for limited or prized resources represents another major parameter of crowding. This covers the spectrum from plants through their root systems competing for a scarce supply of water in the soil, to the overt aggression between two baboon troops over the privilege of feeding on a fig tree, to the not always subtle human competition over such metals as tin, copper or uranium. The agricultural, ecological and socio-political litera-ture, and even the daily press, abound with examples of this aspect of crowding.

Although crowding is a negatively loaded concept, its evalua-tion measures the status of a population. This term, crowding, typifies a characteristic of the English language in which we find a predominance of pathological and negativistic terms. In fact it is difficult to select an appropriate antonym for crowding that becomes appropriate to discussions of population. 'Fulfilling', in the sense of degree of achievement of genetic and cultural potentialities which contribute to the survival of the species, comes closest. The theological-psychological concept of 'be-coming' also has its place as a positively loaded antonym of crowding. The condition which results from crowding is best represented by the word misery, made famous in Malthus's treatise on population. However, a much broader interpretation must be given to misery to include any sort of disease whether it be of physical, biological, social or cultural origin. Thinking positively again often becomes difficult. Well-being is the more common term representing the opposite of misery, but exhaltation and the closely allied concept or process of creativity provide useful handles for evaluating the direction of guiding the course of populations. I have been emphasizing some of the broader aspects of population subsumed under crowding, because unless we consider these broader ramifications it is unlikely that the present focus on alleviating shortages of food and shelter will produce fruitful results.

Two additional parameters which affect the degree of crowding are predictability and arrangement of the physical and social environment. In a completely unpredictable chaotic environment – where it is merely a matter of chance whether a choice leads to gratification of some drive – the misery of frustration prevails only buffered by neurotic irrational justifications for actions taken. At this level of abstraction a completely socially isolated individual can be either crowded or experience some modicum of fulfilment. I shall ignore content of the environment except to note that the absence of accustomed physical and social objects in one's personal space can produce the misery of homesickness and castration anxiety. Arrangement of the physical components of space alters the opportunity for visual, auditory and physical contact among the members of a group or population. In my estimation contact rate among members of a population is the most important variable affecting the status of a population with regard to its social organization and the social well-being of the contained individuals. I shall summarize briefly the salient aspects of this problem which I have developed more fully elsewhere.

Every species of mammal has evolved under some particular set of circumstances in which any individual has a relatively narrow range of numbers of others of its own kind with which it repeatedly comes into contact. Both this number and the con-

figurations and conditions of the environment further establish
a rather narrow range of the number of contacts that each individual will have with its associates. Populations become frag-
mented into groups defined by the fact that each member of the
group tends to have more interactions with other members of the
group than with members of other like assemblies. The average
size of the group, regardless of the causes of its origins, becomes
the optimum size for that group. It becomes the optimum size
because that particular number of individuals permits maximization of gratification from social interaction. Furthermore, the
larger the group size the less intense will be the interaction
between any two individuals. Let us now examine why the
intensity or duration of interaction will decrease as the optimum
group size increases.

Certain types of encounters between animals are mutually
gratifying. Sexual encounters are perhaps the easiest to appreciate.
When both individuals are in a need state for sexual intercourse
their culmination of an interaction places each in a gratifying
refractory state for some period of time during which neither
will seek a comparable encounter. Were either of these individuals
to be approached by another, who was in a need state for the social
interaction of sexual intercourse, neither would respond
appropriately to the sexual needs of others. Where the group
size is small, and encounters thus relatively rare, interaction will
be more intense in order to prolong the gratifying refractory
period to that duration which will make most probable that, when
he is again ready to engage in sexual intercourse, he will
meet another individual who is also ready to respond appropriately. As the group size increases the duration or intensity
of interaction must decrease; otherwise with the increasing
frequency of contacts any individual in a need state will more
likely meet another who is in a refractory state, either gratifying
or frustrating, and will for this reason not respond appropriately
to his advances. This logic derives from empirical observations
codified and supported by detailed mathematical formulations.
Through a long evolutionary history of a particular group size
and rate of contact among members, behavioural and physio-

logical adaptations occur which facilitate the realization of the appropriate number of contacts with the correspondingly appropriate degree of intensity of interaction, and which allows the individual to tolerate the inevitable frustrations which do occur. In fact the maximization of gratification produces an equivalent degree of frustration.

This 'normal' amount of frustration becomes a desirable stimulating necessity. Decrease in group size below the normal, or more specifically a decrease in contacts below the normal, reduces both the amount of gratification and frustration. Increase in group size above the optimum, or increase in contact rate above that characteristic within the optimum sized group, decreases gratification, and increases frustration above the optimum.

Maximizing the effective utilization of resources within the environment culminates in a heightened probability that certain optimum-sized groups will develop through evolution. These form an ascending series: 12, 27, 48, 75, 108, 147 ..., in which after the third members in the series each additional optimum group size is six more than the prior difference in group size added to the prior group size. Of this series the optimum group size of 12 is by far the most prevalent among mammals and probably holds true also for primitive gathering-hunting man. It must be noted that when I speak of an optimum-sized group I am only speaking of the adult members. The younger individuals are being conditioned to assume roles in a group, but for the purpose of defining optimum group size they do not count.

Even in an optimum-sized group, chance factors alone will lead to some individuals experiencing more frustration than gratification. To the extent that any individual experiences more than the optimum degree of frustration, behaviour becomes more deviant and the individual becomes characterized by a greater degree of both physical and psychological withdrawal from socially relevant stimuli or stimuli situations. In my studies of wild and domesticated rats these alterations are expressed by a reduced frequency of leaving places of retreat and entering those situations where social interactions most often occur, and by entering such places at times when more socially active individuals have retired to rest. As withdrawal takes place sequences of activities, such as required in caring for young, become disrupted. Similarly, such withdrawing individuals exhibit an increasing incapacity to utilize appropriate stimuli to trigger behaviour. For example as males begin to withdraw they approach females regardless of their state of estrous or receptivity. With further withdrawal they mount juvenile females, an action normal males never exhibit. Then other males are included as targets for sexual advances; any target will suffice so long as it is a rat, and in such very withdrawn wild rats I have seen them ejaculate from pelvic thrusting over a stone which contained estrous scent on its surface. In the final stage of withdrawal all sexual behaviour drops out; it is as if no object can be detected as appropriate for sexual advances.

This entire spectrum – from completely adequate behaviour to a nearly total absence of participation in social activities – can be seen in even an optimum-sized group. However, as the group size begins to exceed the optimum, more individuals begin to exhibit more marked behavioural aberrations and more extreme degrees of physical and psychological withdrawal. On a theoretical basis at least, when the group size attains the square of the optimum, all members of the group have become so withdrawn that no individual is aware of its associates despite continual proximity to others.

In the normal course of growth of a population segmented into groups, whenever any group increases to nearly twice the size of the optimum number for a group, it splits into two groups. One of these must seek a vacant space in which to establish itself. In so long as the carrying capacity of the environment has not yet been reached, this division of over-large groups prevents the origin of those stresses and excessive degrees of withdrawal characterizing groups having considerably exceeded the optimum group size. Once the carrying capacity of the environment is approached, further division of groups becomes impossible, and thus the members of more and more groups encounter all the difficulties inherent in an excessive number of contacts with associates. Normally there follows a population crash accompanying a reduced ability of individuals to tolerate infectious diseases or the heightened psychological stresses associated with increased density.

Only one species, *Homo sapiens*, has been able to avoid the consequences of this inability of the group to split and to return to the more desirable state provided by life within an optimum-sized group. He has done this by increasing his conceptual space so that the sum of the available physical and conceptual space provides a doubling of the total available space until it harmonizes with the doubling of the group size. We may take 12 adults, along with an average of three living progeny per female, as the composition of the optimum group size of the most primitive gathering-hunting band along the human lineage. I wish now to explore the general pattern of how acquisition of conceptual space permits enlargement of the group size and thus the total population within a particular area. I wish to point out that I am now theorizing with a particular objective in mind; to determine what the optimum population of the human species on this planet might be. So far we have had no criterion for the upper limit of the human population other than calculation of how many mouths we can feed. But it does appear that maintaining a constant density in total space, physical plus conceptual, provides some insight into what the ultimate optimum population for man may be.

When a people with a particular cultural tradition move into an area which is vacant of their kind and they possess the capability of establishing themselves there, each village established will increase in numbers until it reaches the doubling point. At this time it will divide and one group will establish another village. This process will continue until considerable territory is filled with similar villages. Examination of the literature on the historical populating of South and Central America has suggested that 'culture areas' are initiated from a pattern of 61 neighbouring villages as shown in Figure 1. The distance separating villages will be that of their greatest distance apart at which a uniform utilization of resources will occur. This distance is here approximated at 14·25 miles, which leads to a figure of nearly 100 miles across the cultural area encompassing 12,494 square miles.

Once this area is filled with villages, each with an average size of 30 individuals (12 adults and 18 children), and adjoining culture areas are similarly constituted, there is no place to go when further population increase occurs. Population growth does occur though. When each village size doubles, the accommodation to this increased density requires enlargement of conceptual space. In this they develop new roles and social institutions which facilitate the recognition and function of these roles, and they

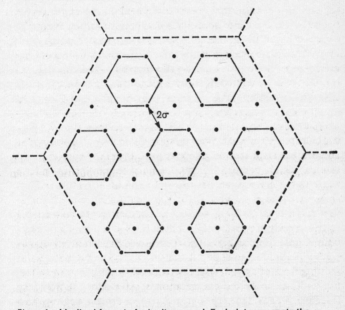

Figure 1. Idealized format of a 'culture area'. Each dot represents the location of a village site. The dashed lines delineate the bounds of the culture area. Six similar culture areas adjoin the one shown. Villages are uniformally spaced at 2σ, where σ is a measure of distance, and is the σ of the bivariate normal distribution function. The central village of the culture area represents its capital, and the central village of each of the surrounding 6 smaller hexagons represents a district focal point.

develop new technologies for more efficient utilization of resources. Of critical importance is the structuring of the group in such a way that the daily contacts of the average individual will have a frequency and intensity much like that which characterized the most primitive state when the optimum group contained 12 adults on the average. This frequency of interaction must be maintained through all future cultural development.

By continuation of this process of enlarging conceptual space successive doublings of the population can take place; each village can double its number of inhabitants several times. We know from the historical record of both the Americas and other regions of the world that eventually neighbouring culture areas begin to coalesce into some larger aggregate which might be termed a nation or empire. The problem is to recognize the point at which further increase in the total population within a culture area can continue no longer by the process of increase of conceptual space generated by its own members. The history of city states, as examples of culture areas, provides one lead. However, as my point of departure I wish to take the experience of the red-bearded Alvarado when in the early 1500s he moved to conquer the culture area of what is now western Guatemala. He was met by an army he estimated at 30,000 troops. From my studies of the groups which comprise small mammal communities I have come to the conclusion that the more dominant members form seven-twelfths of the group. I have made the jump to assuming that seven-twelfths of the adult male population of a culture area form the body of warriors. Eight doublings of the population of a culture area from its base of 30 individuals in each of the 61 villages will lead to a total population of 234,240 and a mobilizable fighting force of 27,328, with the latter being perhaps a more real figure of the suspected exaggeration of Alvarado. We may take this figure of 234,240 as the optimum upper limit of a culture area before the process of coalescing of culture areas begins.

Thirty million square miles can be taken as a fair approximation of that portion of the earth's surface that might be filled with culture areas. If so filled we would have 2,401 culture areas. Further doublings of the population requires coalescing of all the other six culture areas which adjoin some particular one, and must be accompanied by an increase of conceptual space in the realms of social institutions, and technologies which will then harmonize with this increased number of individuals. By this process of coalescing of seven of the physical areas of the prior level of advance in conceptual space with each doubling of the population we eventually arrive at a single world socio-political organization containing nearly 9,000,000,000 persons. This process is summarized in Table 1. However, with a stable population in view we may anticipate approximately 2·2 children per female rather than the three used in all the above calculations. This will give a stable population of slightly over 7,500,000,000 as the optimum world population based upon the above logic. I will grant that this judgement of an optimum is based upon some rather gross assumptions and logic that I have not fully spelled out here. My point is that there can be a logical basis for arriving at a projected optimum human population by integrating developing knowledge of psycho-social processes with the observed history of cultural evolution.

In any case the optimum population of man, or the larger-than-present total world population that will be reached, will impose problems of maintaining the remaining biota of the world. In recent years persons concerned particularly with the preservation of the biota other than man have made value-judgements about what the world population of man should be. It seems to me that their value-judgement is one which essentially says: 'The number of humans on the earth should decrease to the level it was at the year of my birth.' This seems to be a much less tenable position than to explore the more general question: 'At what level of human numbers can the continued evolution of the remaining biota continue?' In the projections above towards an optimum human population of 7,500,000,000 it was assumed that at least 25 per cent of the earth's land surface could be preserved for primary utilization by other forms. However, present trends of human use of land is producing smaller and smaller compart-mentalization and isolation from each other of tracts preserved for other forms than man. This reduction in size of natural areas

Table 1 Theoretical population growth associated with doubling of population with each coalescing of seven of the prior levels of socio-political organization and accompanying increase in conceptual space.*

Socio-political unit	Number of contained culture areas per unit	Number of units	Unit population	World population	Theoretical date
'Culture area' at 'city state' level	1	2,410	234,240	562,410,240	1650
'Nation'	7	343	3,279,360	1,124,820,480	1850
'Empire'	49	49	45,911,040	2,249,640,960	1930
'League'	343	7	642,754,560	4,999,281,920	1985
'World Union'	2,401	1	8,998,563,840	8,998,563,840	2010

*This formulation assumes complete similarity of phasing of development over all time over all the world. In a more general application to the real world coalescense of 'city states' into 'nations' begins with the local development of a technological-scientific revolution paralleled by comparable increases in philosophical conceptual space.

and their isolation from each other will function as major factors in the termination of evolution as it has occurred in the past. To reverse this process of inhibiting evolution we need to establish a broad new policy of land use. The human use of terrain has developed into a meshwork of roads adjoined by less intense use of land connecting intense use areas such as cities. In the interstices of this meshwork lie the natural areas that still exist. Lacking in many instances are channels of communication between natural areas. To develop these more effectively than they exist at present requires that where the channels of human communication cross those between natural areas, the human channels must go over or under the ones between natural areas.

By this type of value system we may develop compatibility between the continuing human adventure and the preservation of evolving biota other than man.

Bibliography

Andrewartha, H. G., *Introduction to the Study of Animal Populations*, University of Chicago Press, 1961.

Appleman, Philip, *The Silent Explosion*, Beacon Press, Boston, 1965.

Browning, T. O., *Animal Populations*, Harper and Row, New York, 1963.

Calhoun, John B., 'Population Density and Social Pathology', *Scientific American*, 206:32, 139–46, 1962.

Calhoun, John B., 'The Social Use of Space', pp. 1–187 of Wm. Mayer and R. van Gelder (eds.), *Physiological Mammalogy*, Vol. 1, Academic Press, New York, 1964.

Calhoun, John B., 'A Glance into the Garden', in *Three Papers on Human Ecology*, Mills College Assembly Series, Mills College, California, 1966.

Christian, J. J., and Davis, E. E., 'Endocrines, Behaviour and Population', *Science*, 146, 1550–60, 1964.

David, Henry P. (ed.), *Population and Mental Health*, Springer, New York, 1964.

Erikson, Erik H., *Insight and Responsibility*, Norton, New York, 1964.

Francis, Roy G. (ed.), *The Population Ahead*, University of Minnesota, Minneapolis, 1958.

Hardin, Garrett, *Population, Evolution and Birth Control*, Freeman, 1964.

Hauser, Philip M., *The Population Dilemma*, Prentice-Hall, New Jersey, 1963.

Richards, I. A., 'The Secret of "Feedforward"', *Saturday Review*, 1968, pp. 14–17.

Several authors: *Population Studies: Animal Ecology and Demography*, Vol. 22, *Cold Spring Harbor Symposia on Quantitative Biology*, The Biological Laboratory, New York, Cold Spring Harbor, 1957.

Wolstenholme, Gordon (ed.), *Man and His Future*, Little Brown, Boston, 1963.

Wynne-Edwards, V. C., *Animal Dispersion in Relation to Social Behaviour*, Oliver & Boyd, 1962.

The Growth of World Population

W. Brass

Population Expansion in the Past 5,000 Years

The realization of the importance of the number of persons in a community must have come early in man's development. Food supply and availability of mating partners, military strength and cooperative activities all depended on the size of the group. Attempts to count the persons (or at least adult males for war or tax purposes) in populations of considerable size also have a long history. There may have been censuses of a kind in ancient Egypt and China; certainly enumerations on a large scale were organized by the Greeks and Romans. It is only in recent times, however, that systematic censuses, covering a substantial proportion of the world's population, have become regular events. Even now, because of incompleteness of coverage, deficiencies of enumerations and time lags from the last census, there is a fair margin for error in the estimate of the number of people living on the earth. As we go further back in time the assessments become progressively more speculative. Rough guesses based on indirect evidence account for an increasing part of the total; in the earliest periods crude magnitudes are arrived at from assumptions about the densities of population which could be supported with the existing primitive methods of food production. Despite these shortcomings the broad movement of population size over the past few thousand years can be traced with reasonable confidence because changes have been sufficiently large to swamp the inaccuracies. The trend in total numbers over time is shown on an ordinary linear scale in Figure 1 and also on a logarithmic scale in Figure 2.

In round numbers the world population was 3,500,000,000

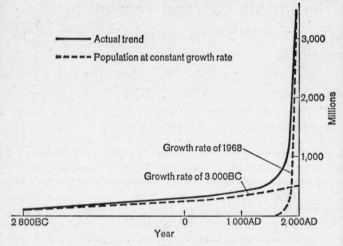

Figure 1. Trend in World Population Growth on Linear Scale.

in mid-1968. This is some 12 times the total at the birth of Christ but three-quarters of the rise has taken place in the past 200 years. The increase has been so much greater in more recent times than in the preceding millenia that the epochs combine awkwardly on a graph with a single linear scale. The major change is squeezed into a small interval towards the present day. If the rate of population increase remains constant, that is a fixed proportion of the total is added each year in what is called geometric growth, the additional number per year goes up with time in any case because the rate is applied to a larger and larger total. In the world as a whole, however, the rate itself has been rising. This is illustrated by the geometric growth curves in Figures 1 and 2 which represent population sizes at the rates of the year zero and 1968 starting and ending respectively with the totals in these years. On the logarithmic scale of Figure 2 a trend of constant growth rate appears as a straight line; the accelerating rate for the world population is then clearly seen.

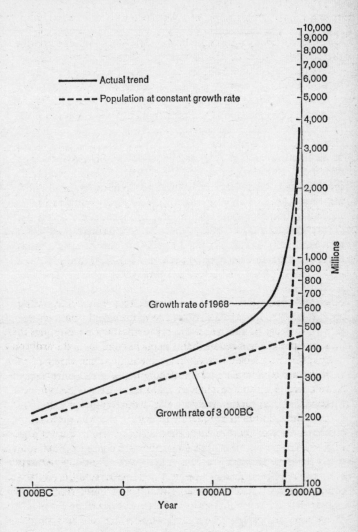

Figure 2. Trend in World Population Growth on Logarithmic Scale.

Determinants of Population Growth

Because of the long time range and the deficiencies of the statistics the representations in the figures appear as smooth curves. In reality there should be wobbles, troughs and peaks corresponding to periods of prosperity, famine, disease, war and other more obscure influences. Any attempt to explain the factors which have stimulated and controlled the growth of world population must ignore these because of inadequate knowledge (except to a limited extent in recent centuries) and concentrate on the broad trend. If we stand far enough away and generalize sufficiently widely, a convincing explanation is easy. With each of the major revolutions in technology, from food gathering to group hunting, from hunting to pastoralism and agriculture, from peasant cultivation to mechanization and industrialization there has been a relaxation of the constraints on food supply which limited population densities. It is usually assumed that in primitive communities the number of children born by each woman is near the maximum that is biologically possible and that birth-rates are thus relatively fixed. With improvements in food supply the death-rate goes down and the growth rate, therefore, up. The variation in timing and extent of changes in different parts of the world would ensure that the effects of the technological revolutions on population growth were gradual rather than abrupt.

Despite the plausibility of this explanation, the attempt to establish its components in convincing detail meets with many difficulties. Over the past ten years or so there has been more thorough and accurate study of the demography of primitive communities. It seems reasonable to believe that the population characteristics of these groups should give clues to man's past history. The pattern that appears is much too complex for simple interpretation. In particular the influence of social and perhaps even psychological factors becomes dominant. Thus, in all the communities studied the average number of children born to women over the reproductive period is much lower than the maximum possible. Variations among groups which are very similar in their ways of life are also considerable. An important element in the determination of the fertility level is the custom in the breast-feeding of babies. While the mother is lactating and giving little supplementary food to the child the probability that she will conceive again is reduced and these intervals of lowered fertility are long in some populations. Practices such as polygamy, the temporary return of the wife to the home of her parents after the birth of a child and the leaving behind of the nursing mothers during parts of the travels of a nomadic pastoral tribe also have an effect. The search for correlations between broad economic and social features and the levels of fertility or of child mortality has not produced any notable clarification or ordering of the diversity.

Population Changes Since 1750

The closer examination of the determinants of population size in more primitive communities shifts the emphasis from the more directly biological factors to social habits operating in a complex manner. Our knowledge of what has happened in developed societies in recent times is, of course, more extensive and accurate although it is important to realize that the period of greater certainty is only a few units of man's life span or even of the generation interval of some 30 years. The replication of experience, which is so necessary in the establishment of associations

Table 1 Estimates of the Population of the World by Regions, 1750–1968.

Region	Population (millions)					
	1750	1800	1850	1900	1950	1968
World total	791	978	1,262	1,650	2,517	3,481
Asia (excluding the U.S.S.R.)	498	630	801	925	1,381	1,945
Africa	106	107	111	133	222	332
Europe (excluding the U.S.S.R.)	125	152	208	296	392	457
U.S.S.R.	42	56	76	134	180	238
North America	2	7	26	82	166	223
Latin America	16	24	38	74	163	267
Oceania	2	2	2	6	13	19

	Annual rate of increase (per cent), 1750–1968				
	1750–1800	1800–1850	1850–1900	1900–1950	1950–68
World total	0·4	0·5	0·5	0·8	1·8
Asia (excluding the U.S.S.R.)	0·5	0·5	0·3	0·8	1·9
Africa	0·0	0·1	0·4	1·0	2·2
Europe (excluding the U.S.S.R.)	0·4	0·6	0·7	0·6	0·9
U.S.S.R.	0·6	0·6	1·1	0·6	1·5
North America	*	2·7	2·3	1·4	1·6
Latin America	0·8	0·9	1·3	1·6	2·7
Oceania	*	*	*	1·6	2·1

*Doubtful growth rates in relatively small numbers are not shown

and gauging of influences, is very limited. Table 1 gives estimates of population size and rates of growth for regions of the world from 1750. For 1900 and earlier I have taken the 'medium' estimates of the range of variants prepared recently by J. D. Durand; for 1950 and 1968 the United Nations statistics have been used (in the latter year after slight extensions to bring them up to date). The choice of different estimates in the range of alternatives constructed by other scientists would not have altered the import of the subsequent comments.

The points to note are the tremendous leap in the rate of growth of world population from 1950, although the trend had been steadily upwards before that and the contrast between what are now usually called the more and the less developed areas, the rich and the poor. To bring out the difference the estimates for Europe, the U.S.S.R., North America, Japan and Oceania have been combined to give measures for the more developed areas which are compared with the corresponding quantities for the rest of the world in Table 2. Over the past century the growth rate in the developed regions as a whole has not varied greatly but that for the poor countries (which contain about 70 per cent of the world population) has risen steadily, with a sharper leap over the past twenty years.

Table 2 Population in the More and Less Developed Regions of the World, 1850–1968.

	1850	1900	1950	1968
	Population (millions)			
More developed regions	343	562	834	1,038
Less developed regions	919	1,088	1,683	2,443
	Per cent annual rate of increase from preceding date			
More developed regions	–	1·0	0·8	1·2
Less developed regions	–	0·3	0·9	2·1
	Share of world total population (per cent)			
More developed regions	27	34	33	30
Less developed regions	73	66	67	70

The more developed regions are taken to be Europe, the U.S.S.R., North America, Oceania and Japan; the less developed are Asia (excluding Japan), Africa and Latin America.

Trends in Birth- and Death-Rates

The relative steadiness of growth in the developed areas conceals profound changes in the determining components, the birth- and death-rates. (Migration although important for particular countries has not distorted the pattern appreciably in large regions and will not be considered here.) Both birth- and death-rates have fallen greatly although the size and timing of the declines have varied in different countries. It is convenient to illustrate the trends by the measures for England and Wales, because of its long history of accurate reports of vital statistics. These are traced in Table 3. The fall in the recorded death-rate began in the 1870s although it seems likely that there was an earlier decline in the eighteenth century before the beginning of registration. The birth-rate fall came a decade or so later but it was steeper with a resulting narrowing of the natural increase, that is the growth when migration is excluded. In some developed

Table 3 Average Annual Birth, Death- and Natural Increase-Rates in Ten-year Periods; England and Wales 1841–50 to 1951–60.

Period	Birth-rate per thousand	Death-rate per thousand	Natural increase per cent
1841–50	32·6	22·4	1·0
1851–60	34·1	22·2	1·2
1861–70	35·2	22·5	1·3
1871–80	35·4	21·4	1·4
1881–90	32·4	19·1	1·3
1891–1900	29·9	18·2	1·2
1901–10	27·2	15·4	1·2
1911–20	21·8	14·4	0·7
1921–30	18·3	12·1	0·6
1931–40	14·9	12·3	0·3
1941–50	16·9	12·4	0·5
1951–60	15·8	11·6	0·4

countries the fall in mortality was later and the birth-rate decline less sharp, with a consequent widening of the natural increase in the more recent periods. For the developed areas as a whole the birth-rate is now about 20 per thousand population per year and the death rate about 9 per thousand.

For the poorer countries of the world the United Nations estimates give a birth-rate at present of roughly 40 per thousand per annum and a death-rate of 18, corresponding to a natural increase of 22 per thousand or 2·2 per cent per year. In my view, these estimates are all a little too low because of deficiencies in the statistics. It is generally assumed that the increased growth rates of the past 50 years have resulted almost entirely from falls in mortality and that fertility has changed little. The view stems more from a theory of what should have happened rather than sound information. The influence of increased birth-rates due to the impact of Western ways of life on social behaviour, for example on breast feeding and separation of parents, may have been greater than is realized. Nevertheless, the saving of lives has certainly been the dominant effect in the most recent period.

To consider more closely the reasons for the trends in birth- and death-rates it is useful to look beyond these composite measures to the basic elements of mortality and fertility. Probabilities of dying are not the same for each person in the community but vary with many factors; in particular differences by age are enormous. The death-rate is thus affected by the population age structure. The measures for England and Wales in Table 3 show that the crude death-rate has been almost constant since the 1920s. In fact the chances of dying (particularly at younger ages) have continued to fall steadily but this has been offset by the greater number of older persons in the population. Since the age distribution is mainly determined by births over the preceding hundred years or so death-rates are by no means independent of birth-rates. The relation between the birth-rate and the probability that a woman at risk will conceive a child in a particular month is even more indirect. It depends on the proportion of females in the population who are in the childbearing period, their distribution by age within it and also on the frequency and timing of marriage. Demographers use the term 'fertility' to describe actual childbearing performance and 'fecundity' for the biological potential. Two populations may have the same birth- or death-rates but differ fundamentally in the structural components from which these result and, therefore, in the implications for the history of the past and the trends in the future.

Causes of Fall in Mortality

In the long run mortality affects the growth-rate through the proportion of children born who survive to reproduce the next generation. Survivorship proportions are increasing in both the richer and poorer regions of the world. In the developed countries the rise has been going on for a long time (in some for at least two centuries). The probability of surviving to adulthood is now so high (about 98 per cent of female children born now in England and Wales are likely to be alive at age 30 years) that further falls in mortality can have little influence on the long term growth of population. Mortality decreases in the poorer countries began more recently (in much of tropical Africa, for instance, they are in the initial stages) and have been far steeper but the scope for improvement is still considerable. On average in these regions about 65–70 per cent of the children born now survive to 30 years. The broad causes of the lower mortality are sufficiently obvious and can be divided into three groups, namely (a) better and more settled economic conditions including ampler and more efficiently distributed food supplies, (b) public health measures such as improved sanitation and water sources, eradication of disease-carrying insects, mass immunization etc., and (c) therapeutic medicine, hospitals, new drugs and so on. The extent to which each of these groups of factors has been responsible for mortality trends, both over the past two centuries in developed countries and the last few decades in less developed areas, is in dispute. The argument is far from being academic since upon the interpretation depends the strategy of further planning to reduce mortality and the assessment of what the outcome will be for population growth. My own interpretation of the evidence (and it is not an unusual view) is that therapeutic measures have not been an important element in the reduction of the world death-rate, whatever their recent influence on mortality in highly developed regions. The judgement between economic and public health improvements is more difficult because they have both been effective; the balance has varied from area to area and the combined influence is probably greater than either would be separately. Thus the eradication of malaria may reduce mortality less if the level of nutrition is at a desperately low level than when food supplies are better. The attempt to allocate the saving in lives between the two factors is then largely a matter of prejudice. Perhaps the most important conclusion is about possibilities in the future rather than what happened in the past. It seems to me clear that mortality has been greatly reduced by the technology of public health even in some areas where economic development has been slight. There is no reason why this process should have reached its limit, whether or not there is much rise in the standard of living of the poorer regions of the world.

Causes of Fertility Change

The immediate cause of the reduction in fertility in developed countries was the prevention of births by contraception. The techniques used in the earlier stages were not necessarily efficient for the individual couple but their average effect over the population was considerable. Now, in countries such as the United States and Australia the proportion of couples who never use contraceptive techniques at any period of their marriage is small and one in three or four of the women at risk take the highly efficient 'pill'. No case can be made that there has been any lowering of fecundity in modern times. Studies of couples who have not yet become or have ceased to be contraceptors show that the lengths of time to conception would lead to fertility as high as any known, if no family limitation was adopted. Structural changes, particularly in the frequency and timing of marriage, have greatly altered birth-rate movements over limited periods of time although they have not determined the general trend. In fact the tendency towards earlier and more universal marriage, which has been a major social feature of Western societies, has offset and sometimes reversed the effects of wider spacing of children on the birth-rate. Indices, calculated by A. J. Coale to show the consequences of marriage patterns for fertility are given for selected populations at different dates in Table 4.

Table 4 Index of Proportions Married for Selected Populations (per cent).

Population	1870	1900	1930	1960
Sweden	42	41	42	63
England and Wales	51	48	50	71
Ireland	42	31	35	47
European Russia		70	63	62
Bulgaria		73	75	78
United States		58	63	75
Japan			68	58
Taiwan			78	72
India		80	83	80
Mexico				61

The indices which allow for changing fertility of marriage with age were cal-culated relative to the measures for the Hutterites in 1930. For this population the index of proportions married was 70 per cent.

Celibacy and delayed marriage were powerful factors in restraining population growth in developed countries in the middle nineteenth and early twentieth centuries. The under-developed regions on the other hand already have the marriage patterns favourable to high fertility towards which the richer parts of the world are tending, without the same widespread use of family planning. The effect of deliberate adoption of contraception on the fertility and growth-rates of the less developed countries has as yet been exceedingly small.

The reasons for the spread of family limitation are (looking back) obvious in general but obscure in particular. No doubt parents realized that with lower mortality a multiplicity of children was not necessary in order that some should survive to be a help and comfort to them in later years. The burden of education and its value for economic advance of the individual, emancipation of women, competing attractions to life in the home all played some part. We do not know which factors (if any on its own) were crucial, the conditions in which they would operate, the timing and pace of their impact. It is not even clear that mortality falls always preceded the lowering of fertility. Explanations have been further disturbed by recent rises in fertility of marriage in many developed countries, for example the United States, Australia and the United Kingdom. Distributions of family size have also altered greatly. For a time it appeared that many married couples were content to produce one child or no children but the percentage in this category is now going down instead of up; on the other hand large families of 5 or more children continue to become less popular. These complex changes in family building practices are not easy to interpret in simple economic terms; such explanations have been attempted but to me at least without cogency. Social and psychological factors are at least as important.

Methods of Population Forecasting

The size and distribution by basic characteristics of future populations are quantities which underlie most economic planning. Only too often the forecasts are accepted as firm foundations for building schemes of development. In fact possible errors are large. Well-contrived predictions of the future can only come from an understanding of the experience of the past; scientific prediction must depend on systematic methods of extrapolating trends, justified by empirical comparisons of the estimates with the actual outcome. It has been pointed out earlier that accurately measured experience of population trends is limited and knowledge of the determinants even more restricted. There has also been too little retrospective evaluation of the success of different techniques of forecasting.

The simplest and most obvious method of estimating the size of the population in the future is to extend forward the past growth-rates. If they have been relatively constant for some time or if little evidence suggests movement either up or down, the continuance of the current rate of growth can be assumed. There are many countries where demographic data are so unsatisfactory that it is hard to justify any less crude procedure. For the world as a whole or, to an even greater degree, the less developed regions estimates made in this way for any recent period would have been badly wrong. For example a forecast of the world population of 1960 made from the current growth-rate in 1920 would have given a total of less than 2,400,000,000 compared with the actual 3,000,000,000; the rise in numbers was more than double that given by the prediction.

A prescient demographer in 1920 might have detected signs of accelerated growth-rates and decided to allow for the trend in his forecasts. He would, then, have found it necessary to specify how fast the rates would increase, how and when they would level off. An attempt to provide a technique for answering such questions was made at about that time by R. Pearl. He suggested that population size over a long period could be described by a logistic curve, a mathematically defined function representing growth-rates which first rose to a maximum and then fell, ultimately tending to zero and the total numbers towards constancy. If, for any given population, the right time scale and point on the curve could be determined the future course would be known. Pearl's model of population change was suggested by experiments on insects living in environments where space and food were restricted. The growth of human numbers was thus assumed to follow biological laws. The logistic curve was much studied and applied with enthusiasm but with disappointing results. In practice the fixing of the time scale and appropriate point on the curve for a particular population were so uncertain even with good statistics that the ideas could hardly be tested. The method is not now seriously in use. Nevertheless, it was a genuinely scientific approach to population prediction and, from a long enough viewpoint, may have some validity. If the focus is narrowed to a more operational time span, however, socio-economic and psychological influences obscure and distort the long-term pressures.

Component Techniques

The procedure for estimating future populations which is now almost universally applied is the 'component' method. As the name indicates, separate consideration is given to the various demographic characteristics upon which the growth-rate depends. The forecasts for each of these are then put together in a consistent way to give the required totals. In its simplest form, the estimates needed are of probabilities of dying by age and sex and rates of childbearing by age of mother. Starting with the current sex-age structure of the population the probabilities of dying adopted for the next period of convenient length (usually a one-year or five-year interval) are applied to find the numbers of survivors; similarly the rates of childbearing give the new individuals. Thus the sex-age distribution one interval later is constructed and repetition of the process with the rates predicted for each time period provides a series of forecasts. The components can be broken down further, e.g. probabilities of marriage and fertility within marriages of different durations by ages of couples can be introduced. The advantages of the method are that the trends in the components may be more clearly seen, assessed and perhaps explained than their compounded effects. For example, in developed countries much of the fluctuation in birth-rates has been due to changes in frequency and timing of marriage; fertility within marriage has been more stable. Marriage rates have now risen so high in countries such as Britain and the United States that few persons will remain single; the scope for further increases is very slight. The separation of these components thus reveals important stabilities and restrictions which aid in estimating the future. A history of accurate measures of components is, however, rarer than good data on population size, and demographic insight may have poor materials on which to operate.

Reliability of Forecasts

The record of success in population forecasting is not impressive even in countries with good data. In 1950 H. F. Dorn wrote a classic paper called 'Pitfalls in Population Forecasts and Projections' which was a devastating criticism of the performance, practice and attitudes of demographers. Although there have been major improvements in understanding since then and some developments in techniques, they have not been accompanied by increasing confidence in prediction. Indeed greater knowledge has made clearer the insecure foundations of past methods and the need for caution and humility in the future. In the Background paper on 'Future Population Trends' prepared by I. B. Taeuber for the 1965 United Nations Population Conference there are many examples of this viewpoint. Thus she writes, 'The inability of demographers to predict future changes accurately or perhaps the inherent unpredictability of such changes has led most of the makers of projections to prepare several alternative series', and 'neither mortality nor fertility are predictable in any precise use of the word'.

One consequence of this lack of confidence has been a confusion of words by which demographers have tried to avoid the labelling of calculated population sizes of the future as firm estimates while retaining the responsibility for giving guidance. 'Forecasts', 'predictions', 'projections' have all been used in different senses.

In particular a 'projection' is properly simply a computation of how the population would change under specified assumptions without any implication about their reasonableness. Although this meaning has not been completely lost, demographers now tend to take it as understood that the word 'favoured' goes with projection, that is, the specified assumptions are regarded as reasonable. A related consequence is the common practice of calculating low, high and medium projections. The clear description of what low and high mean in this context is not easy; they certainly do not denote minimum or maximum possibilities. Any explanation has to bring in words such as 'reasonable'. My own view is that the system which has evolved is a useful one but that its purpose, definition and characteristics require more exposition. Lacking as we do any satisfactory, precisely determined method of extrapolating the population trends of the past into the future, we must on the basis of experience formulate a range of likely alternatives. Although two equally competent persons are liable to arrive at different estimates because their interpretation of experience and what is meant by 'likely' are not the same, it would be a mistake to dismiss the results as mere guesses. The method of approach and the choice of components for making the projection are based on much scientific study and progress is being made in the systematic description of past population changes in a variety of conditions.

United Nations Population Projections

The ranges of population estimates, to the year 2000, from the United Nations' most recent projections are shown in Table 5 for the regions of the world. For mortality a continuing decline is assumed with all regions following the same course but over different sections according to the starting point. The distribution of probabilities of dying by sex and age are specified by a series of hypothetical patterns based on observations for populations with different incidences of death. It is taken that the expectation of life at birth (that is the average years lived by someone born into the population) will increase by half a year annually until expecta-

Table 5 Range of Low to High Estimates of the Population of the World by Region, 1968–2000.

Region	1968	1980	1990	2000
World total	3,481	4,147–4,551	4,783–5,690	5,449–6,994
Asia (excluding the U.S.S.R.)	1,945	2,345–2,619	2,715–3,315	3,103–4,067
Africa	332	434–463	546–629	684–864
Europe (excluding the U.S.S.R.)	457	467–492	482–526	491–563
U.S.S.R.	238	269–296	297–346	316–403
North America	223	248–275	274–323	294–376
Latin America	267	362–383	446–522	532–686
Oceania	19	22–23	25–29	28–35

	Annual rate of increase (per cent)			
	1950–68	1968–80	1980–90	1990–2000
World total	1·8	1·5–2·2	1·4–2·2	1·3–2·1
Asia (excluding the U.S.S.R.)	1·9	1·6–2·5	1·5–2·4	1·3–2·0
Africa	2·2	2·2–2·8	2·3–3·1	2·3–3·2
Europe (excluding the U.S.S.R.)	0·9	0·2–0·6	0·3–0·7	0·2–0·7
U.S.S.R.	1·5	1·0–1·8	1·0–1·6	0·6–1·5
North America	1·6	0·9–1·7	1·0–1·6	0·7–1·5
Latin America	2·7	2·5–3·0	2·1–3·1	1·8–2·7
Oceania	2·1	1·4–1·9	1·3–2·1	1·1–1·9

tion 55 years is reached, a little more rapidly to 65 years and beyond that more slowly again. There is evidence suggesting that the pattern and pace of the decline in mortality should be varied among countries, but a case can be made that the variation is too small and uncertain to be worth taking into account. At least the mortality projections are based on an effectively universal experience of improvements in survival, over a long period in the developed countries and, strikingly, although for a shorter time, in the poorer ones. In addition the effect of future mortality changes on growth is limited by the falls that have occurred previously and the insensitivity of the relation when death-rates are low, which has already been discussed. The inclusion of a reasonable range of alternatives for the mortality component of the projections would have a comparatively small effect on the population sizes and none has been incorporated.

The fertility component is more speculative. In the developed countries, falls in fertility followed those in mortality. Many demographers used to believe firmly in the transition theory which held that in some inevitable way birth-rates would decline after death-rates had begun to do so, in a cycle of economic development. With a fuller realization of the complexity of the socio-economic and psychological influences on fertility, the power of medical technology to reduce death-rates quickly and the difficult economic problems of rapid population growth, faith in the transition theory as a useful tool for projection has notably waned. In the less-developed regions there is little sign of any trend towards lower birth-rates. Nevertheless there are strong pressures for the reduction of fertility operating through the improved survivorship of children, spread of education, employment difficulties and large scale family-planning programmes, some of them heavily backed by governments. These pressures are likely to have an effect but the timing and extent are doubtful. For the United Nations projections it was assumed that the fertility of developing countries would decline to half the present level over a period of 30 years. Dates, varying from country to country, were chosen for the start of the fall. The high, medium and low projections were constructed by taking alternative dates for the initiation of the continuous fertility decline.

A respectable case can be made for the proposition that the high projection is not high enough, that even the latest dates chosen for the commencement of the fertility decline stem more from hope than evidence. Forecasts of larger future populations have been made; if fertility were held at the 1968 level the numbers in the year 2000 would be more than 7,500,000,000. Few demographers, on the other hand, would class the low projection as other than optimistic, although many would share both the optimism and the belief that it was the right descriptive term – that is, that the world would benefit from a rapid reduction in the population growth-rate. Nevertheless, the United Nations estimates do provide a likely range. Whatever point we accept on that range (or even modestly outside it) the population sizes and the growth-rates are formidable. The prospects are particularly frightening for the poorer regions, as can be seen from the estimates in Table 6 and Figure 3; these countries will contain

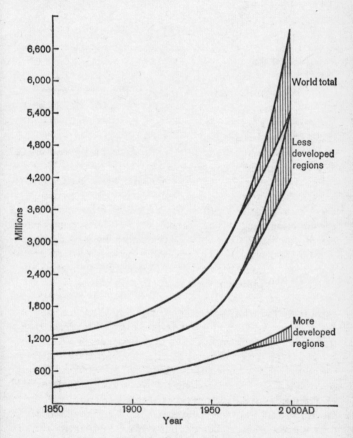

Figure 3. Projections of World Population Growth to the Year 2000.

Table 6 Range of Low to High Estimates of Population in the More and Less Developed Regions of the World, 1968–2000.

	Population (millions)			
	1968	1980	1990	2000
More developed regions	1,038	1,106–1,203	1,186–1,352	1,245–1,516
Less developed regions	2,443	3,041–3,348	3,597–4,338	4,204–5,478
	Per cent annual rate of increase from preceding date			
More developed regions	1·2	0·5–1·2	0·7–1·2	0·5–1·1
Less developed regions	2·1	1·8–2·6	1·7–2·6	1·6–2·3
	Share of world total population (per cent)			
More developed regions	30	27–26	25–24	23–22
Less developed regions	70	73–4	75–6	77–8

nearly 80 per cent of the world population by the end of the century compared with the present 70 per cent.

Population size and structure have usually been regarded as independent measures to be forecast in order that developments dependent on them can be assessed, e.g. economic growth, consumption, need for services and so on. To a greater and greater extent population characteristics are becoming also dependent variables as control over both mortality and fertility increases and deliberate decisions become more important. A population forecast can itself influence what future growth will be since it is a factor in the formulation of social and economic policy and specifically the effort devoted to family limitation programmes. We could profitably modify our attitude to population projections further and begin to regard them as components in a wider network of developmental planning, in which each part reacted on the others. Possible systems (or models) of change could then be constructed for consideration and action. Such an approach would meet great difficulties because of lack of knowledge about the inter-relations of the many elements. The present procedure does not avoid these difficulties but only sweeps them in with the total uncertainty.

Bibliography

More detailed studies of the statistics and of technical problems are contained in these reports and papers.

Dorn, H. F., 'Pitfalls in Population Forecasts and Projections', *Journal of the American Statistical Association*, 45, pp. 311–34, 1950.

Durand, J. D., 'The Modern Expansion of World Population', *Proceedings of the American Philosophical Society*, Vol. 3, 3, pp. 136–59, 1967.

Taeuber, I. B., 'Future Population Trends', Background paper A.4/8/E/453 for the United Nations World Population Conference, Belgrade, 1965.

World Population Prospects as Assessed in 1963, United Nations, New York, 1966.

Many general books on population have sections on estimates and projections. The name of one useful broad survey and also of one older book with interesting materials on population history are given.

Carr-Saunders, A. M., *World Population – Past Growth and Present Trends*, Clarendon Press, 1936.

Hauser, P. M., and Duncan, O. D. (eds.), *The Study of Population: an Inventory and Appraisal*, University of Chicago Press, 1959.

Population Growth and Food Supplies

Ester Boserup

Can the output of food be raised at a rate sufficient to match the increase in world population in the two or three decades ahead which can be confidently predicted? It is difficult to formulate a question more crucial in terms of human welfare, for the prospect implied in a negative answer is the terrifying one of mass starvation. But the reader should appreciate from the start that no clear-cut and confident answer can be given. While the rate of population growth can be foreseen with some certainty within the time horizon indicated above, the rate at which food production may increase depends on unpredictable political factors, such as the preservation of a reasonable amount of political stability in developing countries and the granting of sufficient amounts of foreign aid to the agricultural sector in these countries.

In the following pages an attempt is made to discuss some of the main factors that appear to determine agricultural progress, apart from the crucial political factors mentioned above. The trend from 1950 to the present serves as a general background, and the emphasis is on three sets of factors: the expansion of food production that can be expected in more or less automatic response to population growth, the scope for wider application of scientific methods in agriculture in developing countries, and the impact of economic policies with particular emphasis on the roles of foreign trade and foreign aid.

The Impact of Population Increase on Food Production

Since the middle of this century, food production in the world as a whole seems to have been growing at an annual rate of about 3 per cent. It is seen in Chart 1 that the growth-rate was slightly higher in developing regions (i.e. Latin America, Africa and Asia) than in the industrialized regions (i.e. North America, Europe, including the U.S.S.R., and Oceania), except for the years 1965 and 1966, when the figures for developing regions were heavily influenced by the unusually poor harvests in India. China is not included in the chart, since no reliable production statistics are available; but according to recent F.A.O. estimates food production in China may have increased by more than 4 per cent a year in the period 1961–6.

Reasonably reliable figures for world food production are not available for years before 1950, but there is no doubt that the rate of growth before the middle of the century was much slower than in the more recent period covered in Chart 1. It is important to note, however, that this increase in the rate of growth of food output, a common feature for the two parts of the world, is to be explained by quite different forces in the developing and in the industrialized countries.

In the developing world, population was growing at a considerably slower rate before than after the middle of the century. The increase in rates of population growth is the main factor explaining this increase in the rates of growth of food production. A quite different picture is found for the industrialized part of the world, which can be regarded in broad terms as those countries where the decline in mortality was a secular, gradual process and where, therefore, rates of population increase have remained

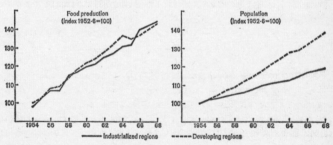

Figure 1.

fairly constant. It appears from the second half of Figure 1, that population growth in the industrialized countries has remained at the usual moderate rate of about 1 per cent, while in the developing countries population is now growing by about $2\frac{1}{2}$ per cent annually. (This figure again excludes China, where the rate of population growth is probably somewhat lower.) Thus, food production in developing countries is increasing at a rate slightly higher than population and in the two years of Indian harvest failure it was increasing less than population.

By contrast, in the industrialized regions of the world, food production is increasing much more rapidly than population, and here the rise in the rate of increase of food production after the middle of the century has little relation to population growth. It is a result of technical progress in agriculture. The use of scientific methods and of industrial inputs have been spreading widely and rapidly in the agrarian sector of the industrialized countries. The resulting increase of productivity was accompanied by a reduction of both the area under cultivation and the labour force in agriculture, but in many industrialized countries this decline in the proportion of economic resources devoted to agriculture was insufficient to avoid production rising at a higher rate than the demand for food. Thus emerged the problem of 'burdensome surpluses' of agricultural produce in North America and Europe. The countries concerned disposed of the surpluses either by export subsidies for food or by giving food away in foreign aid programmes. As a result, food consumption in developing countries could increase at a somewhat more rapid rate than their own food production.

Increase of Subsistence Production

As already mentioned, the increase in production of food in developing regions after 1950 was caused primarily by the increase in the number of mouths to be fed. Most of the rural populations in this group of countries are producing food which is used mainly to feed themselves and their families. When these families grow larger, with declining mortality, they must produce more food than before. Some subsistence farmers do so by migrating from their own village to distant uninhabited or sparsely populated regions. A large share of the expansion of food production in the Philippines, for instance, was obtained by peasants who migrated from the densely populated island of Luzon to the sparsely populated island of Mindanao. But this is a rather exceptional case. In most developing countries, the rapid increase of subsistence production after 1950 was obtained by villagers remaining in their own villages, sowing or planting an ever larger share of the land surrounding the village.

In most developing countries, typical villages are surrounded by large areas of grazing land, bush land or land lying fallow, where new plots can be created when the village population is increasing. During recent decades of rapid population growth fallow and grazing land has gradually been taken under permanent cultivation and the usual fallow periods have been shortened, thus making it possible to cultivate more land each year than was done when the village population was smaller.

In some parts of south and east Asia, population density is much higher than in other developing regions. Many experts therefore believed that there was no further scope for an expansion of the areas under cultivation. It would seem that they were overlooking or underestimating the still considerable possibilities of changing from one to more crops per year on the same piece of land. In China the practice of taking more than one crop every year on a given piece of land has been spreading further and further to the North. In India, where double cropping was little used in the colonial period, it is estimated that nearly one-fifth of the increase of agricultural production in the period 1951–61 was obtained by the introduction of double cropping on land which had hitherto borne only one crop per year, and nearly two-fifths were obtained by cultivation of land which had before been grazing or fallow land. In more sparsely populated regions of subsistence agriculture, for instance in black Africa, nearly all of the increase of subsistence production was obtained by cultivating more land around the villages.

When the increase of food production takes place by expanding the area sown each year, methods of production are likely to remain more or less unchanged. Hence the input of labour in agriculture and output are likely to increase at about the same rate. In other words, the result of population growth in villages where subsistence production prevails is that employment in agriculture increases while output per man engaged in agriculture changes little. Thus, the type of agricultural expansion which is taking place under pressure of increasing numbers of subsistence producers is strikingly different from the one we have been experiencing recently in industrialized countries. There, production expanded concurrently with a decline of agricultural employment which implied that labour productivity in agriculture was increasing very rapidly.

When the expansion of subsistence food production takes place mainly by gradual extension of the area under cultivation, food production expands roughly in step with the increase of rural population. But not all the young people growing up in rural areas of developing countries stay in their village to cultivate land. Many are attracted to the towns and in the period since 1950 the urban population has been increasing at remarkably high rates in virtually all developing countries. This is not the place to suggest economic, historical and sociological explanations for this worldwide trend of migration from country to town. But we must note the important corollary as regards food supply: if food production increases at the same rate as the *rural* population while the urban population increases at a far higher rate, a gap may develop between total demand for food in towns and villages and total food production.

In a country which has no possibilities for importing food (or for reducing exports of food) the opening of such a gap must tend to push up food prices. This may induce the more progressive and enterprising farmers to expand the production of food for sale, and it may likewise tend to discourage the migration of young villagers to the towns. Such a development has in fact been observed in many developing countries, sometimes spontaneously, sometimes with the help of government support, but in other developing countries the gap has been closed by increasing imports of food from industrialized countries. It appears from Figure 2 that imports of cereals to developing countries were increasing rapidly over the last decade, while exports of cereals from developing countries increased at a much lower rate. In the years of Indian harvest failure, 1965 and 1966, the net transfer of cereals from industrialized to developing countries reached a level of 4–5 per cent of consumption in developing countries.

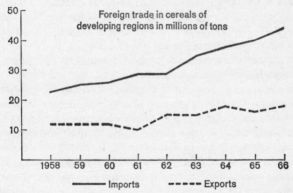

Figure 2.

The Scope for Expansion

Experts who take a pessimistic view of future trends in food production in developing countries point to the great extension of the cultivated area that has taken place already. Some of them suggest that the area of grazing and fallow now remaining must be of very poor quality, others think that the continued process of reducing fallow land and grazing areas must end by spoiling the fertility, not only of the crop land but also of the remaining grazing land, which would deteriorate as a consequence of overgrazing.

Are such gloomy expectations warranted? The answer hinges on the view one takes of the prospects for the adoption of new agricultural methods. There is little doubt that rapidly increasing populations in emergent countries cannot continue for long to draw their food from the available land without a change-over

to methods which preserve better the fertility of the land used
for feeding human beings and animals. On the other hand, with
appropriate changes in methods there seems still to be much scope
in most developing countries for reduction of fallow and cultivation of what are now grazing area. The great majority of domestic
animals in developing countries are left to find most, if not all, of
their feed themselves on land which has never been improved by
human effort. Even in a densely populated country like India
much land could be saved partly by producing feed and hand-
feeding animals and partly by investing in improvement of the
areas where animals are grazing or browsing.

As regards the increase of cultivated area through reduction
of fallow, it must be noted that there are two distinct reasons for
having land lying fallow: the risk that fertility may be reduced
by frequent cultivation, and lack of humidity in the soil. These
handicaps can be eliminated by the use of chemical fertilizers and
of artificial irrigation, respectively. Thus, fertilizer and irrigation
have the effect not only of multiplying the yields of a given crop,
but they make it possible to change over from agriculture with
fallowing to agriculture with annual crops or perhaps with more
than one crop each year.

It should be clear from what has been said that as far as
physical resources and technical potentialities are concerned there
is no reason to doubt that food production can be made to increase in step with population growth in the remaining decades
of this century. The real problem is one of human attitudes and
of economic policy: can the food producers in developing
countries be given sufficient inducement to make the necessary
changes in their methods of production ?

Experience from recent years allows a little cautious optimism.
In some developing countries considerable change has already
taken place in methods of food production, and in such countries
food production has been growing at rates of 5–6 per cent
annually. In all developing countries together (except for China)
consumption of chemical fertilizers has been increasing by 12
per cent per year in the period since the beginning of the 1950s.
Developing countries still use only some 10 per cent of world

fertilizer consumption; thus there is still enormous scope for continued progress and it is expected that the rate of growth of fertilizer consumption will become still higher in the future and that more of the fertilizer will be used on areas under food crops, while in the past the export crops took the larger part of available fertilizers.

Likewise the area equipped with modern irrigation facilities has increased enormously in developing countries since 1950, and F.A.O. experts have projected for the period 1965–85 that the area equipped for irrigation in developing countries may expand by around 2 per cent annually. Moreover, new strains of wheat and rice have been developed in research stations in Mexico and the Philippines. Large increases of crop yields are expected as these new varieties are introduced in developing countries.

The problem remains whether progress in modernization will be held up by failure to carry out the necessary changes of land tenure. Poor tenants with little or no security of tenure may have neither the means nor sufficient incentive to use modern inputs in agriculture. It is not possible to answer this question in a short article. Needless to say, the structure of ownership, rules of tenure and size of holding are crucially important factors for progress in the production of food. But situations in this respect differ enormously as between the various parts of the developing world and, more important, many of the moves towards land reform that have been carried out, or are contemplated, are motivated by social considerations of equity rather than by desire of increasing output. Hence, the effect of land reform on overall productivity in agriculture is often something purely incidental and, in the short run at least, it may be negative as well as positive.

Food Imports as an Alternative to Production

Expenditure on food accounts for a large share of the incomes of most urban families in developing countries. Hence, governments are under considerable pressure to prevent a rise of food prices, if necessary by imports of food. As mentioned above, food surpluses have been emerging in industrialized countries, and this made it easy for governments in developing countries to use food imports to counteract increases in prices of home produced food, since the food could be made available as a gift from the surplus countries, or at subsidized prices. Thus, the wish of governments in developing countries to avoid price increases for food tied in with the wish in industrialized countries to prevent a decline of food prices and farm incomes.

In those developing countries where food production expanded more or less in step with the increase of rural population, but not sufficiently rapidly to feed also the migrants to the towns, an increase of food prices compared to wages and to prices of other products and services would have been unavoidable without the food imports. The higher prices for home grown food would have made it more profitable for cultivators to recruit labourers among the increasing village population and grow food for sale. By contrast, when food imports resulted in a low level of food prices in urban areas, it was less profitable to grow food for sale. Thus, landowners had insufficient incentive to recruit labour for commercial food production.

The persons who benefit from the transfer of food surpluses from industrialized to developing countries are farmers in the industrialized countries, who get rid of their production at remunerative prices, and urban populations in developing countries who benefit from low prices of food. The persons who must pay the bill are cultivators in food-importing emergent countries, who get less production and income from their land, and agricultural workers in developing countries, who get less employment than they would if food imports were smaller.

India provides an interesting example of the effects of food prices and food imports on home production of food. During the first decade after 1950, the Indian government succeeded in holding down food prices in the towns by means of official sales of cheap food, when necessary supplemented by imports. At the same time, measures were taken to promote better methods in agriculture and introduce a more intensive use of land, for instance by improved methods of paddy cultivation. But in spite of the fact that a countrywide extension service was created as a means of bringing the new policy to the farmers, progress was slow until the policy of cheap food prices broke down under the pressure of inflationary price developments in the early sixties.

When Indian food prices began to soar, and particularly after the very poor harvests in 1965 and 1966, it became profitable to employ labourers to expand food production, to irrigate land, to apply fertilizers and other purchased inputs to food production. As a result, the élite among the farmers – literate persons who before preferred to leave the villages for the towns – have been motivated to expand food production. This new development may enhance social tension in the Indian villages: those who first see the new possibilities are the best educated and usually also the richest of the villagers. They are the ones who make use of the government aid put at the disposal of the villages, and their new prosperity is inevitably resented although it is often accompanied by an expansion of employment and thus by an improvement, however modest, of conditions for the poor villagers. At the same time, the high food prices create dissatisfaction in the urban population. There seems to be no blueprint for 'development without tears'.

In discussions about population growth and food production much attention has been given to India's problems. It is widely thought that this huge, densely populated and extremely poor country provides a typical case of 'Malthusian overpopulation'. There is a danger of over-simplification in this view; it is important to note that food production has been raised very considerably in many of the densely populated countries in the Far East, while some of the countries which could not possibly be described as overpopulated have become more and more dependent on food imports.

It can be seen from Figure 3 that food production in the densely populated parts of Asia has moved in step with or exceeded population growth (apart from the two years of Indian harvest failure) while food production in Latin America has expanded less. This is remarkable since there is scope for very large expansion of production in Latin America, especially in those countries where food imports have been increasing rapidly (like Brazil) and in

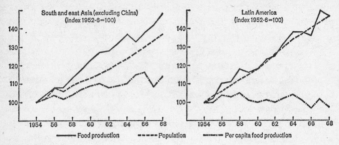

Figure 3.

those where food production has increased least (like Uruguay and the Argentine). In Brazil (as in many sparsely populated African countries), commercial production of food was given insufficient encouragement, because the towns were supplied with imported food. In fact, some of the developing countries where food production is lagging behind population growth are *not* countries where subsistence production predominates, but countries with considerable commercial food production and food exports. Production and exports in such countries suffer by the competition from subsidized food production in the industrialized countries. Thus, net transfers of food from industrialized to developing countries have increased partly because some developing countries have become more dependent on food imports and partly because the industrialized countries have become more self-sufficient in food.

Foreign Aid to Food Production

Most programmes of foreign aid give little emphasis to agriculture. It is true that some big irrigation projects, among them the Aswan Dam in Egypt and the Indus Project in Pakistan, were financed partly by foreign aid, and it is also true that some aid-giving countries, for instance France and England, have been sending a considerable share of their agricultural technicians to developing countries. Nevertheless, aid to agriculture is a relatively small item in total foreign aid budgets. It seems to account for only some 10 per cent of total aid in recent years.

Aid was perhaps less necessary as long as food production could expand on the basis of traditional methods, by cultivating a larger area each year. But when further expansion in the area sown becomes dependent upon the adoption of new methods, for instance the use of fertilizer or the introduction of produced fodder, foreign aid will be increasingly necessary as a means of acquiring the new inputs and attracting the foreign technicians to demonstrate the new procedures. If all this had to await the training of local people and the creation of local industries, agricultural output in many countries would develop too slowly to match the rapid growth of population.

Thus, the new situation entails both danger and challenge: the improved methods that are now becoming indispensable make agricultural expansion more dependent on foreign aid than before, but provided such foreign assistance is forthcoming the new methods promise a more rapid expansion of output per man than was possible in the past when food production increased mainly by a wider application of traditional methods. In this way, possibilities for producing food surpluses for use by urban populations may gradually improve, and the improvement of rural living standards may become more pronounced than in the past. In this process, however, there is one important drawback: in developing countries with a dense and rapidly growing population it may prove difficult to provide sufficient supplies of animal protein, in spite of possible improvements in breeds, in feeding methods and in fodder production. It is fortunate that concern with this problem has already led to the discovery of methods for producing protein-rich food from soy beans, mineral oils and other cheap materials as a substitute for animal proteins of the traditional type. This new development can be seen as the first move towards the longer-term solution of the problem of growing food for increasing populations: the industrial and synthetic production of food. But to pursue this would take us beyond the problems of the near future and indeed beyond the era of agriculture.

In discussions of population growth, the problem of finding employment for the increasing numbers is sometimes stressed more than that of food supplies. The reasoning seems to be that farmers in developing countries are likely to become more and more under-employed when the future expansion of production must rely mainly on the use of fertilizers and other industrially produced inputs. But this would seem to be an unnecessary worry, for this industrial input will be used not to improve crop yields on a sown area of unchanged size, but to enable the sown or planted area to be expanded considerably by the elimination of fallow and by the change-over to production of more than one annual crop on a given area. Therefore, the area under actual cultivation will continue to expand in nearly all developing countries and there should be a corresponding increase of employment for those villagers who do not migrate to the towns. A regular decline in the total demand for agricultural labour in a given country can be expected only when population growth has slowed down or, indeed, when a stage of economic development has been reached where the label 'developing country' does not apply.

Bibliography

Boserup, E., *Conditions of Agricultural Growth. The Economics of Agrarian Change under Population Pressure*, Allen & Unwin, 1965.

Clark, Colin and Haswell, M. R., *The Economics of Subsistence Agriculture*, Macmillan, 1967.

Food and Agriculture Organization, 'The State of Food and Agriculture', Rome, 1969.

O.E.C.D., 'The Food Problem of Developing Countries', Paris, 1968.

Ohlin, Göran, 'Population Control and Economic Development', Paris, 1967.

Schultz, Theodore W., 'Economic Crises in World Agriculture', Ann Arbor, 1965.

Schultz, Theodore W., 'What Ails World Agriculture?', in *Bulletin of Atomic Scientists*, Chicago, January 1968.

Population Regulation in Primitive Societies

Burton Benedict

When anthropologists use the rather unfortunate word 'primitive' to refer to a society, they usually have in mind four criteria: (a) that the society is relatively small in scale, (b) that it has a simple technology, (c) that it is homogeneous in the sense that there are relatively few roles to be played in the society, and nearly every adult male and female can perform nearly every adult male or female role, and (d) that the society lacked, at least until fairly recently, a written language. Though a number of contemporary primitive societies show technological similarities with prehistoric societies, they exhibit such a wide variety of social organization that we cannot say to what extent they are like or unlike societies of the past. This must hold for factors affecting population growth. We do not know whether palaeolithic man had any kind of homeostatic process for controlling population such as Wynne-Edwards (1962) has suggested. A few contemporary primitive societies seem to be concerned with limiting their populations. The vast majority do not. Indeed in most primitive societies there is great emphasis on producing the maximum number of children.

My problem in this short paper is to investigate those factors in primitive societies which affect population growth. What social customs or aspects of the social structure in primitive societies affect population growth? Under what circumstances and by what means do people attempt to limit the growth of population? I shall begin with a brief survey of some of the factors which are believed to affect human fertility in a number of societies. Then I shall look in a general way at those social factors which operate to make people in most societies desire to maximize the number of their offspring. Lastly I shall look at those societies or sections of societies which have attempted to limit their populations with some reference to Wynne-Edwards's stimulating ideas about population regulation in relation to social behaviour.

It must be stated at once that the information we have about population regulation in primitive societies is extremely poor. Very few anthropologists have been concerned with this problem. Their interests have been in outlining the social structure, recording social customs and examining the political, economic and religious aspects of the societies they have studied. The quantitative data they have collected on population growth or decline have not been very systematic or complete, nor have they been collected in such a way as to make comparisons from society to society possible. Moreover, most anthropological studies have been synchronic, studying the society in question at a single period of time, the one or two years during which the anthropologist was in the field. For most of the societies studied there are no reliable historical records. Therefore, in most cases, it has not been possible to examine trends or changes in population growth.

A Cross-Cultural Survey of Factors Affecting Fertility

These limitations appear clearly in a cross-cultural survey of factors affecting human fertility in non-industrial societies published by Nag (1962). Over and over again the correlations he attempts between fertility and various social customs seem to lack significance because the data are inadequate, but they do enable us to divide the factors affecting fertility into at least three types:

(a) Physiological factors such as sterility and venereal disease (which are, of course, linked), diet and length of fertile period. I shall not be dealing with these, though clearly they are important, for as health conditions improve one may expect greater fecundity as well as a higher survival-rate of children born.

(b) Unconscious social factors. These are factors deriving from social customs which affect fertility, but which are usually not regarded by the people themselves as affecting fertility, such as age at marriage, the incidence of separation or divorce, absence of a spouse, widowhood and widow remarriage, polygamy, post-partum sexual abstinence, abstinence during certain seasons or ceremonies and temporary or permanent celibacy by some members of the population.

(c) Conscious social factors affecting population growth such as voluntary sexual abstinence, contraceptive practices, abortion and infanticide.

Unconscious Social Factors Affecting Fertility

Let us now examine some of the unconscious social factors. In many ways this is an unsatisfactory procedure, for it means removing certain customs or practices from their cultural matrix. What appears to be a similar practice may have very different meanings in different societies or be correlated with other factors which may negate or enhance its effect on fertility. In general the evidence that these unconscious social factors limit population growth is far from conclusive.

(a) Age at marriage. Late marriage does appear to reduce fertility, the classic instance being Ireland. In other societies the age at marriage does not seem to be significant in affecting fertility. In some societies, for example in India, marriage may occur before puberty but sexual relations do not normally occur until after puberty. In others, for example in the West Indies, marriage occurs late, but regular sexual relations and the production of children may precede marriage. In this case, insofar as couples do not set up a household together, sexual relations may be at irregular intervals and lead to reduced fertility. In most primitive societies marriage occurs early. Two types of explanation may be relevant here: the evolutionary and the social structural. Compared to most other animals human beings reproduce slowly. They usually produce only one offspring at a time and this offspring is peculiarly helpless and takes a great deal of parental care before it reaches self-sufficiency. The infant mortality rate in primitive societies is extremely high, so that early unions ensure that the female will conceive a maximum number of offspring during her years of fecundity. Not only is infant mortality high in primitive society; mortality in general is high and the life span short. Thus from an evolutionary stand-point early marriage would seem to promote survival of the species.

From the point of view of the social structure many primitive societies are characterized by lineage, clan and/or joint family organization. Such social forms place great emphasis on con-tinuing the line, on producing heirs for property and succession to office. This concern motivates people to arrange early marriage for their offspring.

(b) Polygamy. When anthropologists talk about polygamous societies, they mean societies in which polygamy (either poly-andry or polygyny) is permitted, not that it is the statistical norm. Polygamous marriages are virtually always a minority of mar-riages.

Polyandry is so rare and the information about it so meagre that we can say very little about its effect on fertility. The Toda and the Jaunsari, the two polyandrous societies listed by Nag, show no significant difference in the fertility levels of polyand-rously and non-polyandrously married women.

Most investigators have thought that polygyny reduces fertility, but Lorimer (1954) thinks the opposite. The great difficulty is to determine the extent of polygyny within a given society. Nag's data do not support an association between poly-gyny and reduced fertility, but he is comparing a whole society in which polygyny is practised with one in which it is not. A better procedure, as he himself admits, is to compare fertility levels of polygynously and monogamously married women within a single society. Dorjahn (1958) did this for some African societies and claimed that polygyny does reduce fertility, but this conclusion is not confirmed by tests of statistical significance according to Nag (page 92). Factors which may reduce the fertility of poly-gynous unions are: (1) Lower frequency of coitus per wife. Many societies have rules about the number of nights a husband is required to spend with each wife. (2) Age factors. In most poly-gynous societies it is only older men who have gained enough wealth, power and prestige to take more than one wife. Second and subsequent wives are usually very young women. It is assumed that such older men are less sexually active than young men. At the same time the wives are forbidden sexual relations with other men.

(c) Separation and divorce. Nearly all societies make some provisions for separation or divorce. To see how this affects fertility one would need to know for each society: (1) frequency of separation, (2) age of spouses at separation, (3) frequency of remarriage after separation, (4) length of the interval between separation and remarriage. Though the data are not conclusive, there does seem to be a correlation between a high rate of separation and a low level of fertility. In Jamaica Roberts (1954) has shown that the fertility level is highest in legal unions, second highest in common law unions and lowest in casual or visiting unions. Other factors such as abortion, sterility or frequency of coitus may intervene.

(d) Widowhood. Variables affecting fertility are: (1) frequency of remarriage, (2) the age interval between the husband's death and remarriage, (3) the probabilities of women becoming widows at different ages. Social customs vary from absolute prohibition of remarriage and even the immolation of widows (as in *sati* in India), to compulsory remarriage (as in the levirate which obliges a man to raise seed in his brother's widow). Widow remarriage appears to be correlated with the type of kinship and family structure and with economic factors including class. In general marriage is more stable in patrilineal societies than in matrilineal ones. In the former a woman produces children for her husband's lineage. In the latter she produces them for her own of which her brother or mother's brother is usually the head. Yet if this affects fertility negatively in matrilineal societies (and there is not very good evidence that it does) the effects may be counteracted by the higher incidence of widow remarriage in matrilineal than in patrilineal societies. This shows the danger of isolating such factors as separation, widowhood, polygamy and age at marriage. Clearly, they are inter-related in their effects on fertility.

A more important factor than whether a society is matrilineal, patrilineal or cognatic (without corporate lineages and tracing relationships through both parents) is economic class. In India and China, for example, widow celibacy is usually more strictly enforced among upper classes than in lower classes.

(e) Post-partum abstinence varies from a few weeks to two or three years in some societies. A long period of abstinence does seem to be correlated with lower fertility according to Nag, but there are often other factors intervening such as polygyny. Societies in which coitus is forbidden during lactation often have beliefs that it would harm the child.

(f) Abstinence and menstruation. Belief that coitus should not occur with a menstruating woman is very widespread. A few societies (for example, the Marquesans, the Trukese, the Walapai and the Maori) do permit it (Ford and Beach, page 225). Beliefs supporting abstinence vary from the idea that it is disgusting to notions about the danger and ritual impurity of menstrual blood. In some societies women retire to a special house during menstruation. Orthodox Hindus will not allow a menstruating woman to prepare food for the household. As ova are not released during menstruation, it is unlikely that abstinence during this period affects fertility.

(g) Ceremonial abstinence. In many societies sexual abstinence is associated with religious fasts or rituals, for example, to ensure success in hunting or during periods of mourning. Their occurrence is irregular, but among Hindus it has been estimated that there are about 24 such days per year (Chandraskaran). It is difficult to estimate the effect that ceremonial abstinence has on fertility levels, but it would not seem to be great.

(h) Celibacy. Obviously no society enjoins permanent celibacy on all its members. In most primitive societies celibacy is to be avoided at all costs and no individual remains unmarried unless he is seriously physically disabled or a mental deviant. A number of societies have special roles for such deviants who may become mediums or ritual specialists. In some societies, particularly war-like societies which are organized into age grades, sexual relations may be forbidden to young men in the warrior grade.

Among the Zulus, for example, the king's age regiments were forbidden to marry and were required to live at his capital until, after a number of years, he gave them permission to marry and disperse. Similarly, the plains Indians of North America often went through a period of celibacy as warriors. Sometimes such celibate periods may be organized around religion. Thus in Buddhist countries young men are expected to spend several years as novices during which they should not engage in sexual relations. The effect of such practices is to delay the age of marriage, so it is possible that they have some negative effect on fertility. Again we simply do not have any figures to substantiate this.

Permanent celibacy for significant numbers of a population seems to be confined to complex societies. Permanent spinsterhood in Ireland or in Victorian England, for example, seems to be correlated with economic factors (Davis and Blake, pages 218–22). Permanent celibacy for any considerable number of males seems to be confined to certain religious orders such as those found among Roman Catholics, but it does not appear to have occurred on a scale large enough to affect fertility levels.

(i) Frequency of coitus. It is, of course, exceedingly difficult to obtain information about actual frequency of coitus. Easier to obtain are people's beliefs about frequency. What bearing these have on actual frequencies must remain an open question. A few societies such as the Yap of Micronesia and Juang of Orissa are reported to believe that excessive coitus is harmful, but there is no evidence as to how this affects frequency. The Crow Indians are reported to believe that it is weakening to have intercourse every night, but find it difficult to have it less frequently (Ford and Beach, page 83)! In Nag's sample only among the Yap does a low frequency of coitus appear to be correlated with low fertility. An important variable affecting frequency is age and this is rarely mentioned in ethnographic accounts about coitus. The evidence for frequency of coitus variables is so poor that no conclusions can be drawn. One can only guess that it is unlikely to be so low in the vast majority of societies as to affect fertility significantly.

Conscious Factors Affecting Fertility

Conscious factors limiting fertility involve problems of motivation, so that it becomes even more important to examine the social context in which such actions are taken than was the case with unconscious factors. Our information about the incidence of contraception, abortion and infanticide in primitive societies is meagre. Nag reports contraception as having a high negative affect on fertility in only 5 of the 61 societies which he considers to have factors affecting fertility negatively. Abortion is reported as having a high negative affect in 13 societies, but there is no information for 22 of the 61 societies in the sample. Infanticide is not even listed because the data are so scanty.

(a) Contraception. A fairly large number of primitive societies are reported to use various plants to attempt to produce temporary or permanent sterility in males and females, but their extent and efficacy are not known. A post-coital douche is also reported in a number of societies. However, by far the most commonly reported contraceptive technique is *coitus interruptus*. As Glass (1963) has pointed out, this method was instrumental in the West before modern chemical and mechanical techniques became available, and only in the United States has it ceased to be one of the major techniques employed. Seppilli (1960) reporting on a rural community in central Italy notes a 50 per cent drop in the birth-rate between 1930 and 1950 brought on entirely by increased abortion and contraception through the practice of *coitus interruptus*. It should be noted that this is almost invariably a male-initiated technique, though Schapera (1941) reports that among the Kgatla of Botswana the women sometimes initiate it by moving their hips or turning over as they feel the man nearing ejaculation. He also reports that this leads to quarrels (page 223).

The patterns of relations between the sexes can be studied from at least two aspects which may be put as questions: With whom do sexual relations take place? With whom are sexual matters discussed? These rarely coincide. In many societies one can discuss sexual matters with people, even people of the opposite sex, with whom it would be unthinkable to have sexual relations, and it is often considered highly improper to discuss sexual matters with one's sexual partner, particularly if that partner is one's spouse. A Manus of the Admiralty Islands can make lewd jokes and even fondle the breasts of his female cross cousin, but he may not copulate with her. His relations with his wife are rather strained and formal if not actually hostile. Such attitudes are linked with other factors in the social structure; for example, he is heavily in debt to pay for his marriage, and he may be assisted by his cross cousin (Mead). In investigating motivations for limiting fertility in primitive societies the patterns of communications between the sexes are major variables which have been too often neglected by family planners.

(b) Abortion. Unlike *coitus interruptus* abortion is almost invariably a female-initiated technique. It can often be done without the knowledge of the male. It is very widely reported in primitive societies but is generally socially disapproved, and it is very difficult to say anything about its extent. A further difficulty lies in the failure by many investigators to distinguish between abortion and miscarriage. Abortion may be demographically important in some societies. Schneider (1955) reports it is widely practised on Yap where women are not expected to have children until they are in their thirties. Youth is defined as a period of sexual licence when a woman should not be tied down with children. Frequent abortions by young women sometimes cause sterility. Yap is in fact becoming depopulated. A similar practice seems to prevail in Formosa where Devereux (1955) reports some women had as many as 16 abortions (page 26).

(c) Infanticide. Infanticide allows for selection of personal characteristics of the offspring such as sex and physical condition. Motivating factors can be ritual or economic. In some societies twins are considered unpropitious and one or both may be killed. Other societies consider them a highly favourable omen. Children born unusually, such as children born feet first or with teeth, those whose mothers died at birth, or those who are born on unlucky days, may be killed (Davis and Blake, page 231). Except possibly for a very few societies like the Rendille of Kenya who kill boys born on Wednesday or after the eldest brother has been circumcised (Spencer, 1965), infanticide for ritual reasons would not seem to have much effect in reducing fertility levels.

Infanticide for economic reasons seems to be closely linked with the food supply. It occurs among peoples living in very harsh environments, for example, the Eskimos (Balikci, 1967), or in very restricted environments such as small islands, for example the Tikopia (Firth, 1936), or among those living in great poverty, for example, the Chinese (Fei, 1939). In such societies it is usually female infants who are killed, and this factor is closely linked to other aspects of the social structure. Thus the Netsilik Eskimos kill girl babies (usually by allowing them to freeze, or smothering them) because women do not hunt, are not self sufficient and require years of care only to leave at marriage (Balikci, pages 621-2). The practice is so prevalent along the arctic coast that male children outnumber females by two to one, at least in four groups which were surveyed by Weyer (1932, page 134).

Among the Tikopia of Polynesia infanticide is at the discretion of the father who turns down the face of an unwanted child immediately after birth. Reasons given by informants usually had to do with potential food supplies, though sometimes illegitimacy was a cause. It is not clear from Firth's material whether male or female infanticide was more prevalent, but he quotes an informant who stated: 'The work of the women is to plait mats and fill the waterbottles, and when one or two girls have been born, that is enough! But men go out and catch fish and do other work.' (1936, page 415).

Among the peasant cultivators of the Yangtze plain studied by Fei in the 1930s the smallness of individual holdings meant economic disaster if too many children were born. Abortion was frequently practised as was infanticide. Males were sometimes killed, but it was far more usual to kill females. Fei found a ratio of only 100 girls to 135 boys in the 0-5 age group (page 34). The Chinese kinship system is strongly patrilineal and patrilocal marriage is practised. Thus girls are an economic burden on their parents and leave the household as soon as they are mature. Moreover, they must take a considerable dowry with them on marriage. Patrilineality is strongly reinforced by ancestor worship; only a son can perform these rites for his parents and only a son can carry on the line.

Female infants may not be killed outright, but in families where food is short, sons are better fed. Even where girls do not actually starve, epidemics will be much more likely to carry them off than their better nourished brothers (Lang, 1946, page 150). The situation is similar for India.

This brief survey of conscious and unconscious factors affecting fertility has shown that for the vast majority of societies there are few social mechanisms for controlling fertility, and that those that exist, except in a very few societies, do not appear to be very effective. The fact is that in most primitive societies people do not wish to restrict fertility. On the contrary they desire to produce the maximum number of children.

Social Factors and Family Size

Wynne-Edwards (1962) has shown that rarely among non-human animals do populations expand to the limits of their food supplies so that one finds starving animals. There are intervening social variables which limit such uncontrolled expansion by limiting access to food and mates. One of these is territorial behaviour by which an animal or group of animals marks out a territory which he or they will defend against interlopers of the same species. Another is hierarchical behaviour by which high-ranking animals have priority to food and mates. Though we can find both territorial and hierarchical behaviour among humans, this conspicuously has not led to a control of population. In animal societies we find such social behaviours as territory and hierarchy intervening between the animal's basic needs for food and mates and their satisfaction. In human societies we find a whole host of behaviours intervening and these can be broadly described as culture. But cultural factors do not merely intervene, they tend to define needs. Human needs even in the simplest societies are not confined to food and mates or even territory. They have become elaborated, particularly by considerations of status and prestige.

The Chinese killed girl babies not simply because there was a shortage of food, but because the status and prestige of the family is manifested in the dowry given to a daughter on marriage and because the lineage can only be perpetuated by males. The Tikopia, too, are patrilineal so that only males can carry on the line. Important ceremonies are performed by males and only males hold office. Even among the Eskimo, it is the males who carry the prestige of the domestic group.

When humans attempt to control their populations, individuals, except in the very extreme cases which I have cited, are not inspired by a concern for scarce basic resources but by a concern for scarce social resources, objects or behaviours which give status and prestige, which are, of course, defined in terms of scarcity.

In so far as prestige factors are linked with family size, the emphasis in the vast majority of the world's societies is on the maximum production of children. Lorimer (1954) advanced the hypothesis that corporate kin groups, particularly unilineal ones, generate strong motives for high fertility. What evidence we have seems to confirm this. In societies where there is a strong emphasis on the male line of descent barrenness in women or even the failure to produce a son may lead to the repudiation of a wife. The pressures on women to produce children do not cease after one or two children, and this is due to the high social value of children and the way the production of children is built into the political, economic and social systems of the society. One of the reasons for this is the high infant mortality rate in primitive and peasant societies. High infant mortality is not only the fact in such societies, but also the expectation. Due to the spread of medical services in recent years, the facts have changed more quickly than the expectations.

In most simple societies the lines of kinship are the lines of political power, social prestige and economic aggrandizement. The more children a man has, the more successful marriage alliances he can arrange, increasing his own power and influence by linking himself to men of greater power or to men who will be his supporters. Considerable economic exchanges in cattle in Africa, in shell money, yams and pigs in the Pacific, in produce, consumer goods and money in peasant societies, take place at marriages. The man with many children controls much wealth. In terms of economic production more children mean an increased food supply and perhaps the production of surpluses for trade. Most of the world's religions place great emphasis on the production of children. In primitive societies fertility cults, often linking human fertility with that of natural products, abound. These and many similar practices and beliefs place a high value on children. In primitive and peasant societies the man with few children is the man of minor influence and the childless man is virtually a social nonentity. Some of these customs and beliefs may have a high survival value where the mortality rate is high as they keep the society well supplied with new members. But they are proving disastrous where the mortality rate is low and resources to maintain life are limited.

It is only in societies or sections of a society where status and prestige factors operate against large families that individuals attempt to limit the numbers of their offspring. To return to the example of the rural community in central Italy where the birthrate dropped by 50 per cent in 20 years, we find this to be correlated with marked economic and social changes. In 1930 the community was chiefly engaged in farming. The extended patriarchal family was the norm. More children meant more help on the farm. The economy was basically a subsistence one. By 1950 the community had become almost a dormitory suburb of the nearby town of Rieti where many men and some women worked in factories. Instead of living in large rural homesteads dependent on the produce of the land, many now lived in small houses or flats and were dependent on a wage. To have many children was now seen as an economic hardship dragging the whole family down. The emphasis was on conjugal family living with few children whom it was desired to educate. There was a greater desire for consumer goods.

A significant point to be derived from this and other studies is that it is upwardly mobile couples who tend to want to limit their families because they see that this mobility will be accelerated by having smaller families, and they have entered into a system in which prestige factors are not linked to children. The very poor even in industrial societies can often see no advantage in limiting their children. At the lowest levels 10 children are no more of a handicap than 9. The child as yet unborn may be the very one who will help his parents. If a man does not have dependants on whom will *he* depend when he is old and ill? In countries, such as Britain, which pay family allowances, these act as a positive inducement to have children, especially in families where cash is chronically short.

Summary

Wynne-Edwards has shown that in animal societies there are certain mechanisms of social behaviour which tend to control access to food and mates. In a sense status is involved as it is chiefly the high-ranking animals which have this access. Such social behaviour in animals tends to limit population growth. Animals have developed anatomical structures and conventionalized forms of behaviour operating always within the same competitive framework of access to food and mates. Man lives in a highly adaptive social framework in which the objects for which he competes and the very rules of competition can change rapidly. Such social behaviour in man is not necessarily linked to population control. Douglas (1966) has developed this point. She shows for a number of societies that population control is not related to subsistence but to competition for power and prestige. In most primitive societies insofar as scarce social resources are connected with population, they emphasize the production of the maximum number of children. In some sections of industrial and urban societies and in a very few simple societies prestige factors may be linked with small family size. Except under the harshest ecological and economic conditions, human beings do not regulate their populations in relation to the food supply, but in relation to the prestige supply.

Bibliography

REFERENCES

Balikci, A., 'Female Infanticide on the Arctic Coast', *Man: the Journal of the Royal Anthropological Institute*, N.S. Vol. 2, no. 4, 1967.

Chandrasekaran, C., 'Cultural Patterns in Relation to Family Planning in India', *Proceedings of the Third International Conference on Planned Parenthood*, Bombay, 1952.

Davis, K., and Blake, J., 'Social Structure and Fertility: an Analytic Framework', *Economic Development and Cultural Change*, Vol. 4, no. 3, 1956.

Devereux, G., *A Study of Abortion in Primitive Societies*, New York, 1955.

Dorjahn, V. R., 'Fertility, Polygyny and their Inter-Relations in Temne Society', *American Anthropologist*, Vol. 60, no. 5, 1958.

Douglas, M., 1966. 'Population Control in Primitive Groups', *British Journal of Sociology*, Vol. 17, no. 3, 1966.

Fei, H. T., *Peasant Life in China*, Routledge & Kegan Paul, 1939.

Firth, R., *We, The Tikopia*, Allen & Unwin, 1936.

Ford, C. S., and Beach, F. A., *Patterns of Sexual Behaviour*, Eyre & Spottiswoode, 1952.

Glass, D. V., 'Fertility and Birth Control in Developed Societies: Their Relevance to the Problems of Developing Countries', *Family Planning*, Vol. 12, no. 1, 1963.

Lang, O., *Chinese Family and Society*, Oxford University Press, 1947.

Lorimer, F. *et al.*, *Culture and Human Fertility*, U.N.E.S.C.O., Paris, 1954.

Mead, M., *Growing Up in New Guinea*, Pelican Books, 1942.

Nag, M., *Factors Affecting Human Fertility in Nonindustrial Societies: a Cross Cultural Study*. Yale University Publications in Anthropology, No. 66, New Haven, 1962.

Roberts, G. W., 'Some Aspects of Mating and Fertility in the West Indies', *Population Studies*, Vol. 8, 1954.

Schapera, I., *Married Life in an African Tribe*, New York, 1941.

Schneider, D. M., 'Abortion and Depopulation on a Pacific Island', in Paul, B., and Miller, W. B. (eds.), *Health, Culture and Community*, New York, 1955.

Seppilli, T., 'Social Conditions of Fertility in a Rural Community in Transition in Central Italy', in Rubin, V. (ed.), *Culture, Science and Health,* Annals of the New York Academy of Sciences, Vol. 84, art. 17, 1960.

Spencer, P., *The Samburu,* Routledge & Kegan Paul, 1965.

Weyer, E. M., *The Eskimos,* Yale University Press, New Haven, 1932.

Wynne-Edwards, V. C., *Animal Dispersion in Relation to Social Behaviour,* Oliver & Boyd, 1962.

Contraception Today

Ruth E. Fowler and R. G. Edwards

Societies throughout history have made use of various contraceptive techniques. Despite a recurring background of magic formulae, superstition and folklore, some methods were evolved in earlier times that are still widely used today. For example, *coitus interruptus* was used in early societies, is mentioned in Greek, Biblical and Roman writings, and is employed at the present time. Intra-vaginal sponges or douches containing potions such as lemon juice, vinegar, olive oil, dung, gums, quinine, etc., have been utilized for centuries to prevent the entry of spermatozoa into the upper female tract. The condom likewise has a long history, beginning in antiquity according to some historians. Operative techniques on men and women to induce sterility were also familiar to ancient and primitive societies and abortion has been widely practised in the past. More sophisticated methods of contraception were used in the nineteenth century, but rapid advances in knowledge of reproductive physiology have led to new methods of controlling human fertility only during the last 30 years or so. Overgrowth of population could seriously hamper economic development in many countries, and could be limited by national family planning programmes. Family planning associations or similar organizations have existed in some countries for many years. But for too long studies of human reproduction and fertility have been obstructed by widespread ignorance and prejudice. Government action to assist family planning has been restricted to very few countries. The attitude of some religious organizations has done little to help with the problem, while others, notably the Roman Catholic Church, still restrict measures of birth control to the so-called 'rhythm method' or 'safe period'. In many countries there has until comparatively recently been a marked lack of involvement of doctors and scientists in studying and applying contraceptive technology.

Attitudes are now changing fast, a situation almost certainly associated largely with the new status of women in society. The family planning movement owes a great deal to women determined to be free of excessive childbearing and unwanted pregnancies. Yet in this century, pioneers of the movement such as Marie Stopes and Margaret Sanger had a hard fight to establish clinics and promote sex education. Only since the war has rapid progress in organization of the international family planning movement been made. During this period too the development and widespread use of the oral contraceptive pill and of the intra-uterine contraceptive device have to a large extent freed intercourse from conception, a new situation which is certain to have profound effects on social and moral attitudes to sexual behaviour.

When considering the actual methods available today, it is important to realize that no single method is yet suitable for every couple or situation. New methods are needed, especially for the male. An alternation of method between husband and wife would prevent or reduce long-term hazards of contraceptive methods to either one of them. The ideal contraceptive must be safe, acceptable, remote from intercourse, easy to use, inexpensive and readily available. Present-day methods meet some of these requirements, but even the ideal contraceptive will require motivation on the part of the user. We shall describe in this article the conventional or traditional methods as well as the newer ones. Then surgical methods leading to the limitation of fertility, notably sterilization and abortion, will be outlined. Finally, some of the newer approaches under test will be mentioned, but only those that have reached the stage of being tested in man. Failure rates given for each method include unreliability ('method failure') and incorrect use ('patient failure'), and are usually expressed 'per hundred women years of exposure'. This figure gives the ratio of the number of pregnancies in relation to the period that the contraceptive was tested.

Traditional or 'Conventional' Methods

Not surprisingly, the original idea in contraceptive practice was to prevent spermatozoa gaining access to the eggs. Various 'barriers' were devised, or intercourse was restricted in certain ways, in order to achieve this end. These ideas thus represent the elementary beginnings of contraceptive practice. Most of these methods are relatively unreliable, sexually unsatisfactory, and have to be applied at the time of intercourse. Yet even today their use is widespread, which is sufficient comment on the state of our knowledge of ourselves in the age of space research. Abstinence must be considered as a conventional method, for it is practised in some societies for a period after childbirth and might be more widespread than suspected; questionnaires would probably fail to establish that this method had in fact been adopted. Conventional methods practised by the male are *coitus interruptus* and the use of the condom; the object is to prevent spermatozoa entering the female tract. Methods practised by the female include the use of spermicides in the vagina or fitting diaphragms and cervical caps. The object here is to prevent spermatozoa in the vagina from entering the upper female tract. In the rhythm method, intercourse is restricted to the 'safe period' when there is no fertilizable egg in the oviduct. We shall consider these methods in turn.

CONVENTIONAL METHODS FOR THE MALE

Coitus interruptus or withdrawal. This depends for contraceptive purposes on the male retracting from intercourse before the spermatozoa are ejaculated. It is a method widely used, but it is unsatisfactory on two major counts. The failure rate may be high (see Table 1), although other surveys indicate that failure rates may be no higher than for other conventional methods. Many men cannot achieve the necessary control. Even if control is accomplished, some spermatozoa may be shed by the male before orgasm; the method may thus be unreliable even if performed correctly. Secondly, many women fail to achieve their orgasm due to anxiety about the method and to the abrupt termination of intercourse. Despite these disadvantages, the method will no doubt continue to be widely used when intercourse is spontaneous or unexpected. And where the sale of contraceptives is prevented by law, this method remains, sadly, the only one for the male.

Condoms. The penis is enclosed in a sheath before intercourse commences, so that spermatozoa are prevented from entering the vagina. Withdrawal must follow immediately after intercourse to prevent leakage from the end of the condom. Some sources state that the original use of the condom was as a protection against infection. Until the last century, skin or gut from animals was employed in their manufacture, but these materials were later replaced by latex rubber. The most recent development is the manufacture of condoms from plastic material in the U.S.A.; because the plastic is inert they can be stored indefinitely. The mass production of condoms has undoubtedly been a major factor in the limitation of fertility, and this method is still widely used by men. Careful control of the manufacturing process is vital and ensures greater reliability, since defective condoms have been a cause of failure, but leakage is a distinct possibility, and condoms are often used in combination with spermicides for greater efficiency. This method has been accepted by many societies, although in some countries their sale has been prohibited for religious reasons. Although it has proved difficult to estimate the number of couples using condoms since their frequency of use is unknown, not less than 5,000,000 gross are manufactured in the U.S.A. and not less than 8,000,000 gross in the rest of the world.

Condoms have the advantage of being retailed through many and diverse channels, many of them non-medical and even including the local stores! An anonymity is thus offered to prospective purchasers which is often appreciated. Condoms are especially useful early in marriage, where the woman is unable to wear a cap or diaphragm, or where other methods such as the pill or intra-uterine device are not desired. Their effectiveness is moderate, perhaps nearer the lower figure given in Table 1. On the other hand, sheaths dull sensation and delay orgasm for many men, and this lessens their acceptability. Nevertheless, the sale of condoms would seem certain to remain a major factor limiting fertility for many years to come, although perhaps declining with the increase in oral contraception.

CONVENTIONAL METHODS FOR THE FEMALE

Spermicides. Spermicidal agents in the form of foaming tablets, jelly and creams and suppositories are frequently used to prevent conception by killing spermatozoa deposited in the vagina. Preparations available on the market differ in their method of insertion and in the type of base and spermicide employed. Unless inserted shortly before intercourse, their effectiveness diminishes. Even when used carefully, the effectiveness varies; for example, suppositories or jelly and cream alone may be satisfactory for preventing conception in some people, yet the same preparations used by others may prove a complete failure. High failure rates have often been associated with foaming tablets and aerosol sprays, and they are even less dependable than other conventional methods such as *coitus interruptus* or the rhythm method. But despite their low rate of success, these methods have been shown to be immediately acceptable in some parts of the world because of their simplicity of use. The effectiveness of the jelly or creams is substantially increased if used with a condom or diaphragm. More recently, spermicides have been effectively used with the intra-uterine device during mid-cycle when the danger of conception is highest.

Post-coital douches, which were intended to remove spermatozoa from the vagina before they migrate through the cervix, are now considered ineffective. They do not warrant a place among present-day contraceptive techniques.

Diaphragms and Cervical Caps. Diaphragms and cervical caps prevent the migration of spermatozoa through the cervix into the uterus. Several types of diaphragm are available. For effective use, the woman must be taught how to insert the diaphragm or cap correctly and how to check that it is in the right position. Regular visits to the clinic are necessary if the method is to be continually successful. Diaphragms and caps have to be inserted before intercourse and not removed for at least 8 hours afterwards, and a diaphragm can be worn only if there is sufficient muscular tone in the neck of the womb to keep it in place. Cervical caps are mainly fitted when a woman is unable to wear a diaphragm because of insufficient muscular tone or displacement of the uterus; they are more difficult to fit into place than diaphragms, but are designed to be left in place and removed only during menstruation. Both the cap and the diaphragm are used with spermicidal chemicals.

Diaphragms and cervical caps provide excellent protection against conception for some couples but are less effective than originally supposed (Table 1); this may be because of carelessness

Table 1 Reported Failure Rates for Traditional Contraceptive Methods.

Method	Pregnancy rates per 100 years of use	
	High	Low
Coitus interruptus	38	10
Condom	28	7
Spermicides:		
Foams	43	12
Suppositories	42	4
Jelly or cream	38	4
Douche	41	21
Sponge and foam powder	35	28
Diaphragms and jelly	35	4
Rhythm	38	0

Data adapted from A. L. Southam, in (ed.) *Family Planning and Population Programmes*, University of Chicago Press, 1966.

or a failure of the diaphragm itself. Unlike the condom, diaphragms and caps do not diminish male or female sensitivity to any significant extent, and despite its failure to prevent conception in some couples it remains a safe and widely used method which is readily acceptable to many women. It is estimated that about 2,000,000 women in the U.S.A. and about 50,000 in the U.K. use the diaphragm, although its usage has declined sharply since the introduction of the intra-uterine device and the pill. Other major drawbacks in the use of the diaphragm are the necessary visits to clinics, difficulty in its correct insertion for some women, and the anticipation of intercourse. In Britain its use has been largely confined to the middle class.

The Rhythm Method. This method was first described about 50 years ago, and depends on avoiding intercourse during the 'fertile period', i.e. the period in the cycle when fertilization can occur. Its efficiency depends entirely on knowing the time of ovulation, so that the egg and spermatozoa are not in the fallopian tube at the same time. This has proved a major snag in practice. A rise in body temperature during the mid-period of the menstrual cycle, due to the synthesis of the hormone progesterone in the ovary, is taken to indicate that ovulation has occurred. Spermatozoa are generally thought to survive in the female tract for up to three days but they may survive for longer. If the egg is only fertilizable for 24 hours after ovulation, fertilization could only occur following intercourse during four days of each menstrual cycle, and intercourse must therefore be avoided for at least three days before and two days after the rise in temperature. But few women have absolutely regular cycles, so the time of ovulation cannot be predicted with any degree of accuracy. In practice, therefore, intercourse must be avoided between days 10 and 19 of the cycle, according to some authorities. The rhythm method is still extensively used and may prove satisfactory for some, but many couples find it almost impossibly frustrating to confine intercourse to a few days in each menstrual cycle. Many couples will probably change to newer methods of contraception. Nevertheless it is still the only method of birth control approved by the Roman Catholic Church, despite its unreliability (Table 1).

INTRA-UTERINE CONTRACEPTIVE DEVICES (I.U.D.S)

In the last decade, the I.U.D. has emerged as an important method contributing to contraception. Its use has been promoted vigorously by various family planning organizations, and at one time it promised to be the major new method in controlling rapid population growth in developing countries (Table 2).

Table 2 'Targets for India' (millions).

Year	Method		
	Condom	I.U.D.	Sterilization
1966–7	1·83	2·33	1·38
1967–8	3·56	5·09	1·90
1968–9	4·66	8·46	2·57
1969–70	4·66	13·70	3·39
1970–71	4·66	19·69	4·51

Data from B. L. Raina, in (ed.) *Family Planning and Population Programmes*, University of Chicago, 1966.

Many claims have been made that I.U.D.s were used by various primitive tribes. It is said that the ancient Greeks also used them and that Arabs prevented pregnancy in camels by inserting stones into the uteri of females before going on a long journey. Many of these stories remain largely unsubstantiated.

The first intra-uterine device, as we know it today, was described in 1909 and it was used early in the present century, following the work of Grafenberg and others. The early devices took the form of rings made of silver ('Grafenberg ring') or silkworm gut, which were placed in the uterus after dilation of the cervix. But adverse reports caused the method to fall into disrepute. I.U.D.s have recently again returned to favour, stimulated by two reports published simultaneously in Israel and Japan showing them to be effective and relatively harmless when modified from the earlier models. Rapid progress has since been made in this field, and a wide variety of I.U.D.s made of polyethylene instead of metal or gut are now manufactured. Modern I.U.D.s are pulled out straight and loaded into an inserter tube which is passed through the cervix. The I.U.D. is passed through this tube by means of a plunger and when released from the inserter the I.U.D. moves back into its original shape in the uterus. I.U.D.s should always be inserted by skilled staff under sterile conditions so as to reduce the risk of infection and avoid complications at insertion such as perforation of the uterus.

Patients may experience some pain and bleeding at insertion, but the I.U.D. is tolerated well by most women despite heavier menstruation. Some 20–25 per cent of women may abandon this method of contraception within a year (Tables 3 and 4), although these figures are no higher than for other methods of contraception.

A disadvantage of I.U.D.s is that some are expelled naturally from the uterus, but after reinsertion they frequently remain in place (Tables 3 and 4). Women can be taught to check that the device is still in position since most I.U.D.s now in use have an extension thread protruding into the vagina. Larger types of I.U.D.s which are now being introduced are expelled less frequently. This inadvertent expulsion of an I.U.D. was a drawback, for the woman believed that she was still protected against conception.

Table 3 Events per 100 I.U.D. Insertions after One Year.

Events	Korea*	Chile†
Pregnancy	3·9	4·3
Expulsions (first and later)	11·5	20·4
Removals for medical reasons	19·8	6·3
Removals for other reasons	2·9	2·1

*All sizes of Lippes loop combined, mostly loop B. Data modified from *I.P.P.F. Medical Bulletin,* vol. 1, no. 3, April 1967.
†Zipper ring. Data from J. Zipper, M. L. Garcia and L. Pastena, *Proceedings of the Eighth International Conference of the International Planned Parenthood Federation,* p. 302, Santiago, 1967.

Removal of the I.U.D. is frequently requested (Table 3), often because of uterine pain, although this rarely continues beyond the first 3 months. Other reasons for requesting the removal of the I.U.D.s include irregular abnormal bleeding from the vagina and vaginal discharge. There is no evidence that an I.U.D. can cause cancer, although there is a reported risk that

Table 4 Continuation rates, pregnancy rates, expulsions and removals per 100 I.U.D. insertions after several years.*

1. *Lippes Loop D, 1–4 years*

Interval	Cumulative continuation rates		Annual rates		
	Low	High	Pregnancies	Expulsions (including first and later)	Removals (all reasons)
1 year	71	80	2·6	12·1	17·3
2 years	56	70	1·9	4·0	14·6
3 years	47	64	1·1	2·6	11·8
4 years	40	59	1·3	0·7	10·5

2. *Various Devices, 2 years*

Device	Cumulative continuation rates		Cumulative rates		
	Low	High	Pregnancies	Expulsions (including first and later)	Removals (all reasons)
Lippes loop A (small)	60	65	4·7	27·8	30·3
Lippes loop B	42	71	2·4	22·1	28·2
Lippes loop C	48	72	2·0	20·8	25·5
Lippes loop D (large)	56	70	2·1	15·2	28·8
Small spiral	55	62	2·3	43·4	34·2
Large spiral	54	66	1·1	30·6	40·7
Small bow	58	66	8·1	6·0	32·0
Large bow	62	72	3·6	2·9	26·9
Steel ring	52	71	4·5	22·6	22·7

*Data modified from A. Tietze, *Proceedings of the Eighth International Conference of the International Planned Parenthood Federation*, p. 307, Santiago, 1967. Data mostly from the U.S.A.

local inflammation might lead to sterility after the device is removed. The great advantage of I.U.D.s when successfully inserted is the protection they offer for many years without further effort. This is obviously a great advantage compared to the 'pill', which requires daily motivation.

Compared with conventional methods of fertility control, the I.U.D. is highly effective (Tables 3 and 4). In the U.S.A. a failure rate of 1–3 per cent during the first year of use occurs with the better I.U.D.s, although slightly higher failure rates have been reported from some of the less-developed countries. During mid-cycle it is advisable to use the I.U.D. in conjunction with a spermicide. I.U.D.s have proved highly acceptable and several million are now in use. An I.U.D. is inserted easily in women who have had one or more children, but this is a minor factor in its favour compared with the permanence of its protection. The insertion is carried out at a time remote from intercourse, and no further attention is required other than a yearly check-up. I.U.D.s are cheap to produce, although some authorities consider that when the cost of the medical personnel is taken into account it is only slightly cheaper than the 'pill'.

Even today the mode of action of the I.U.D. is not understood. They were at first thought to hasten the movement of eggs down the fallopian tubes, leading to the expulsion of embryos from the vagina. Fertilization was also believed to be suppressed in many women. Current ideas suggest that inflammatory and other conditions arise in the uterus and destroy or expel the embryos before they implant. Since pregnancy does occasionally occur with an I.U.D. *in situ* it is apparent that fertilization can occur, and their most likely mode of action may be to prevent implantation. It is obviously important to establish their mode of action, but this may prove difficult since I.U.D.s have different effects on different experimental animals.

Important and effective means of population control in the family planning programmes of many countries is provided by the I.U.D. They are at present popular in Western and developing countries although probably used more by women who have completed their family.

A study in Taiwan shows that nearly 80 per cent of those seeking family planning advice chose the I.U.D., 2 per cent the oral contraceptive pills and 19 per cent traditional methods. By contrast, of those couples accepting family planning guidance in Korea, only about 25 per cent at the onset of the programme accepted the I.U.D. Traditional methods had an unexpectedly high rate of acceptance. But there is now striking evidence that the I.U.D. has gained in popularity since its introduction and that many who originally accepted traditional methods have now switched to the I.U.D. The Koreans have a goal of 1,000,000 insertions by the end of 1971.

The Lippes loop is the most commonly used device, and has two nylon threads which protrude through the cervix. The Saf-T Coil, a double outward spiral, is also becoming more popular. Lippes loops have been widely used in Taiwan and in Korea. Previous experience with the Ota ring in Taiwan was undoubtedly one reason for the popularity of the Lippes loop, but its effectiveness has been sufficiently high (pregnancy rate 3–4 per cent) to make it acceptable. Although side effects do occur, about 80 per cent of the women can wear the device without trouble. It is also cheap and has the great advantage that it can be removed easily.

ORAL CONTRACEPTIVES

Oral contraception ('the pill') has modified the whole approach to family planning, and its development has been largely due to the work of Pincus and his colleagues in the U.S.A. The action of the pills is to suppress ovulation. They contain mixtures of two types of steroid hormone, called oestrogens and progestins. These steriods can influence the levels of the pituitary hormones called follicle-stimulating hormone (F.S.H.) and luteinizing hormone (L.H.) which triggers ovulation. F.S.H. is secreted during the first part of the cycle, and L.H. in mid-cycle. By adjusting the quantities of steroids ingested, ovulation can be suppressed. Natural steroids were known for many years to exert this effect when taken orally, but this treatment could cause disturbances in menstruation, which is initiated by the declining levels of progesterone at the end of the cycle. Chemical modification of the steroid molecule gave good control over menstruation while inhibiting ovulation, and led to the development of the pill as a balance between an oestrogen and a progestin.

The pills are taken for 20–22 days in each menstrual cycle, with a seven day interval between each course. They are of two types, combined or sequential. Combined tablets contain an oestrogen which is either ethinyl oestradiol or its 3-methyl ether derivative, together with a progestin. Progestins are generally one of several 17-hydroxyprogesterone derivatives, or one of the many 19-norsteroid compounds. In the sequential treatment oestrogen alone is given for the first 14–16 days of the menstrual cycle followed by oestrogen and progestin together to complete the course. The oestrogen components are important for the development of the endometrium (the lining of the uterus), and for inhibiting ovulation, and the progestins also suppress ovulation and are necessary to produce 'withdrawal bleeding' at the end of the treatment. Women may be provided with substitute or placebo tablets between the monthly courses of treatment to avoid the necessity of counting the days between courses.

Both combined and sequential tablets normally inhibit ovulation by suppressing the release of the pituitary gonadotrophins necessary for normal follicular development in the ovary and ovulation of the egg. The action of the pill is probably achieved by effects of the steroids on the hypothalamus or the higher brain centres, which in turn influence the pituitary. Combined pills evidently depress the amount of circulating luteinizing hormone and sequential treatments depress the amount of follicle-stimulating hormone. Combined pills are slightly more effective in preventing pregnancy than sequentials. This may be due to other effects of combined pills, such as effects on the cervical mucus making sperm migration difficult, or on the endometrium promoting a hostile environment for implanation if ovulation should occur.

At the end of each monthly course of tablets, the endometrium is shed and withdrawal bleeding occurs which is similar to normal menstruation. The length of the cycle need not necessarily be restricted to one month, and could be simply controlled by reducing or increasing the number of days on which tablets are taken. Contraceptive pills generally reduce menstrual loss because of the inhibition of ovulation, thus providing an additional benefit for women who normally have heavy periods. Clinical studies have shown the oral contraceptives to be safe, highly acceptable, very effective and reversible in action. They are tolerated well by the majority of users. The most common side effects such as nausea and headaches tend to disappear with time and other more serious side effects, for example, jaundice, thrombo-embolic diseases and abnormalities in carbohydrate and lipid metabolism occur in very few women. The incidence of thrombo-embolic diseases has been some cause for concern, and is higher in women on the pill than in women not taking the pill, but evidently no higher than in pregnancy. Oral contraceptives have proved to be the most effective method of fertility control yet discovered and any adverse effects must be balanced against the hazards associated with unwanted pregnancies, such as abortion or maternal death.

Many different products containing various amounts and types of progestins and oestrogens are now available. This variety is

Table 5 Reasons for Discontinuation of the Pill by Puerto Ricans, in Relation to Age and Period of Use.

Reason	Age (years)		Period of use (months)	
	15–19	30 and over	0–12	25 and over
Marital separation	26·4	28·9	18·3	16·3
Want another pregnancy	12·5	4·4	8·7	16·3
Medical	11·1	19·9	19·0	15·2
Sterilization	5·8	8·9	4·6	3·5
Personal	7·0	9·0	7·6	12·8
Other	19·4	20·0	29·1	15·0
Lost to follow-up	18·0	8·9	12·7	20·9

Data modified from A. Hernández Torres, *Proceedings of the Eighth International Conference of the International Planned Parenthood Federation*, p. 487, Santiago, 1967.

due to efforts made to reduce side-effects to a minimum and to increase potency, so reducing the size and cost of doses. Oral tablets have been used with success in many parts of the world (see Table 5) with a failure rate of 0·2–1·0 pregnancies per 100 women-years. This is a remarkably low figure and surpasses other methods including the I.U.D. The chief disadvantage of the method is that motivation must be maintained to continue daily taking of the pill month after month, and foresight is needed to renew supplies (Table 5). The risk of pregnancy is increased if one or more pills are omitted during a cycle. In Puerto Rico, where clinical trials of oral contraception started more than 10 years ago, studies have shown that many women have switched from the pill to the I.U.D. since its introduction there in 1961. When given a free choice almost equal numbers chose the pill and the I.U.D. Those selecting the pill tended to be younger, have fewer children and used the pill to space their family; whereas those selecting the I.U.D. used it more as a substitute for sterilization. After $3\frac{1}{2}$ years, half of those who selected the I.U.D. were still using it, and only 22 per cent of the original number were still using contraceptive pills (Table 6). Pills can

Table 6 Cumulative Continuation Rates for the Pill.

Country	No. of women	Woman cycles of use	Continuation rates				
			6 mths	1 yr	2 yrs	3 yrs	4 yrs
Puerto Rico	562	12,095	73	57	37	26	23
U.K.	4,383	74,486	90	85	80	73	
Ceylon	651	11,545	90	76	56	35	
India (Bombay)	649	11,763	80†	71	55	30	
U.S.A. (Chicago)	14,157	147,541	83	77	72		
Turkey	2,158	8,167	31‡	12‡			
Taiwan	873	1,809		48			

Data modified from large-scale studies reported by G. W. Jones and W. P. Mauldin, *Studies in Family Planning* no. 24, December 1967. The Population Council, New York.
†7 months.
‡Perhaps underestimates, due to method of collection of data.

obviously be discontinued more easily than I.U.D.s, which require a return to the clinic for removal, and pill taking can be overlooked or ended if the supply inadvertently ends. But it is dangerous to generalize from one country to another (see Table 6) and the use of the pill for fertility control is widespread and increasing year by year. Oral contraception has been accepted and provided far more widely in Western than in developing countries.

Oral contraceptives require far less medical supervision than the I.U.D., and are proving very popular. Over 6,500,000 women are using oral contraceptives in the U.S.A. and the pill may be primarily responsible for the declining birth-rate in that country. More than 6,000,000 women use the pill in other parts of the world and numbers are increasing year by year. The expense of the pill remains a problem in less developed countries, and the I.U.D. provides a cheaper alternative. The use of the pill in national programmes may also be limited if many women fail to continue pill-taking for long periods of time. Further, there is always the question of long term hazards which cannot be fully answered at the present time, so that the search for alternative methods of fertility control must continue. It could well be that the pills presently in use will soon be outdated. We shall return to these potential methods later.

ABORTION

When contraceptive methods fail or are not employed recourse is often made to abortion. Abortion is widespread, the subject of heated debate, condemned by many religions, illegal in many countries, the source of considerable damage to the health of the mother and possibly a cause of psychological disturbance. Yet abortion is a major factor today in family limitation and the restriction of population size. Repressive attitudes can merely make the unwanted pregnancy more disturbing to the mother and make illegal abortion more likely. This equation seems to hold the world over, and the pattern that emerges is largely conditioned by the social attitudes adopted towards abortion.

While deploring the use of abortion as the only means of regulating the number of live births, one has to come to terms with it as a means of ending unwanted pregnancies. It appears that the incidence of abortion will be reduced only by the dissemination of contraceptive knowledge and technique.

Although illegal in many countries, abortion is legalized in others for social or medical reasons. Legalized abortion at least ensures that the operation is performed under adequate medical conditions. In hospitals, abortion is usually performed in the first trimester of pregnancy by curettage, although there are other methods. Recently a new method widely used in China and Eastern Europe has been adopted by some doctors in Western countries. This is the 'suction method' whereby the foetus and placenta are withdrawn as remnants by vacuum aspiration. This method, also performed during the first trimester of pregnancy, is claimed to involve a much lower rate of complications such as perforation of the uterine wall, blood loss, pain, etc. In contrast illegal abortion utilizes a variety of chemicals and devices; perhaps most often a rubber tube is inserted to destroy the foetus. Inevitably, many complications follow illicit abortions carried out under septic and unsatisfactory conditions. Bleeding, clotting, sterility, pain, incomplete abortion and psychological effects are on the gruesome list of complications, and it would appear that the majority of illicit abortions can cause some damage to the mother. Complications also accompany legal abortions in hospitals and clinics, although their incidence is declining with improved services. Data from Czechoslovakia showed that maternal deaths from legal abortions were substantially less frequent than from criminal abortions. In the U.S.A., some 3,000–4,000 deaths annually have been ascribed to illegal abortion, and this accounts for 45 per cent of maternal deaths.

One of the first countries with a widespread programme of legal abortion was Japan, and many operations were performed during the late forties and early fifties. By 1952 the importance of family planning programmes in reducing abortions was appreciated and since their introduction there has been an increase in the use of contraceptives; the present birth-rate

in Japan is among the lowest in the world, due to both con-
traception and abortion. Abortion is also legalized in some
Eastern European countries, including the U.S.S.R., and in
Great Britain (Table 7). The resulting rapid fall in the birth-

Table 7 Legal Abortions in Various Countries.

Country	Year	Abortion rates per 1,000 women aged 15–49 years	Abortion rates per 100 live births
Bulgaria	1964	45	67
Czechoslovakia	1965	22·5	29
Hungary	1965	77	135
Poland	1964	20	32
Yugoslavia	1964	20	37
Japan	1961		65
Japan	1965		46
(U.S.A., estimated illegal abortions)			approx. 20

Data obtained from M. Potts, *Eugenics Review*, 59, no. 4, 1967; G. Nozue, *Proceedings of the Eighth International Conference of the International Planned Parenthood Federation*, p. 129, Santiago, 1967; and E. W. Overstreet, *Proceedings of the Eighth International Conference of the International Planned Parenthood Federation*, p. 148, 1967.

rate in Rumania has led to a repeal of the abortion laws. Hungary
has perhaps the highest rate of induced abortion in Europe, the
majority of conceptions resulting in abortion. The large number
of abortions in some countries appears to be due to the primitive
and inefficient methods of contraception practised there, *coitus
interruptus* being the most widely used method. In Russia, for
example, the 'pill' has not yet been accepted on any scale. Abortion is tolerated in some Islamic countries. In Egypt and Iran the
possibility of damage to the health of the mother is taken into
account; in Jordan and Lebanon, a woman seeking abortion to
save her own or her family's reputation is treated leniently. In
Latin America, abortion laws are strict and many illegal operations are performed. In Mexico, one study revealed that 30 per
cent of women had had one or more abortions. The demands on

hospital services caused by abortion in Latin America are often staggeringly high, e.g. a study in Honduras showed that 47 per cent of the blood dispensed by the Blood Bank was to cases of abortion. Contraceptive practice is in its infancy in South America, and abortion is clearly widely accepted by the population despite repressive legislation. In the U.S.A., it is estimated that there may be as many as 1,000,000 abortions carried out per annum, and there has been much debate about liberalization of the law.

Economic, social and moral pressures will no doubt continue the demand for abortion, since once fertilization has occurred, desperate measures are often adopted. But changing social conditions and attitudes will almost certainly bring about changes in its practice. Educated middle classes are emerging in many countries, and in others the number of illegitimate conceptions is increasing among adolescents. Some women are aborted repeatedly – one report produced a woman who declared 35 abortions. It is to be hoped that ultimately the increasing use of contraceptives will reduce the need for abortion.

STERILIZATION

Sterilization is obviously the ultimate method of suppressing conception. Today it offers a practical and effective method of fertility control especially for couples who have completed their families. The most potent method of all is to remove the gonads, i.e. castration, but this method is totally unacceptable because the secondary sexual characters are profoundly affected. The alternative method is to place a block in the male or female tract. In men the vas deferens is ligated and a small piece excised (vasectomy); this blocks the pathway of the spermatozoa from the testis, and they are resorbed in the vas. The procedure is almost wholly successful, but is also nearly always irreversible, for there is only a small possibility of rejoining the vas should this be desired. Vasectomy is a simple procedure requiring only local anaesthetic, and it would undoubtedly be more popular if it was reversible. At some future time, plastic or other substances might be injected into the lumen of the vas deferens to form a temporary block which can be removed later. In India and Korea vasectomy is becoming widely used in family planning programmes (Table 2), and is having a considerable effect in restricting population growth. Over 450,000 vasectomies have been performed in India between 1956 and 1965, and the total up to the present time must by now have exceeded 1,000,000.

Sterilization of women is usually carried out by sectioning and removing part of the fallopian tubes. As a result, spermatozoa cannot reach the site of fertilization, nor can the eggs reach the uterus. This is not a major operation, but is more serious than vasectomy for it demands opening the abdomen under a general anaesthetic. It seems almost certain that newer methods will be more widely used, for example laparoscopy, a minor operation during which all the manipulations on the oviduct are carried out through a small incision in the body wall. Blockage of the tube is permanent, almost totally successful, and almost certainly irreversible. Indeed, many women are infertile because of an accidental blockage in the fallopian tube, and the chance of a cure is low. Sterilization of women is not usually used except where the family is completed, the number of children large, when pregnancy can endanger the health of the mother or (in some countries) a genetic defect occurs in the family.

Sterilization, especially of the male, is often most welcome to couples who have completed their families, and we are likely to see a large increase in the use of these techniques although long-term effects have not been fully assessed. For example, approximately one third of vasectomized men develop antibodies against their own spermatozoa. Sterilization is also most valuable in family planning programmes. Its permanence means that the patient will have no more children, and problems such as omission of pill taking or removal of I.U.D.s do not arise.

FUTURE DEVELOPMENTS

New methods of contraception are bound to arise. In the near future, it seems almost certain that developments in endocrinology will set the pace, for this field has been well studied. Other possible approaches involve the use of pharmaceutical agents or antibodies. We shall deal with these methods in turn.

Low-Dose Orals. The daily ingestion by women of a pill containing a small dose of progesterone (e.g. chlormadinone acetate) has a pronounced contraceptive activity. Unlike the Pincus pill, these are taken daily, without interruption. The woman's cycle is frequently disrupted, although other side-effects are minimal and the risks of long-term hazards would appear to be less than with the Pincus pill since the dose of hormone is less. The pills contain no oestrogen, which might reduce the risk of thrombosis, and are cheaper than conventional pills. But with a failure rate variously reported as between 3·7 and 9·5 pregnancies per 100 women-years, or even higher, these tablets are less effective than combined or sequential pills, and there is less control of the menstrual cycle. Their mode of action is not understood; ovulation is not prevented, and it is assumed that either fertilization is prevented through changes hostile to spermatozoa in the cervical mucus and uterine secretions, or that the uterine endometrium is altered so that the embryo cannot implant. An interesting extension of this method would be to implant sub-dermally a plastic capsule containing steroids. The hormones would be released very slowly over many years, and so give permanent protection from conception. When pregnancy was desired, the capsule would be removed.

Long-acting Injections. Long-acting progestogens, used either alone or combined with oestrogen and given as intramuscular injections each month, inhibit ovulation. Side-effects occur and good control of the menstrual cycle has not been achieved. Larger doses of a progestogen (medroxyprogesterone acetate) injected at 3 or 6 month intervals completely change the menstrual pattern for some months, but many women might find this change unacceptable. At present there are major snags with this method, even though it is highly effective in suppressing conception. Irregular bleeding, nausea and nervousness are experienced by some women. A considerable interval is required after the injection for normal cycles to reappear, although nearly all patients ovulate within one year.

The Post-Coital Pill. A contraceptive pill to be taken after intercourse would obviously be most valuable. Small-scale trials involving the oral ingestion of 2·5 mg. ethinyl oestradiol, or 25–50 mg. stilboestrol for 4–6 days, or every other day for three days, after intercourse have proved very promising. Most of the significant work with this method has been done on primates and other animals. The oestrogens might exert their action by causing the rapid movement of the embryo down the tubes or by suppressing implantation of the embryo. Such a pill might be developed, but the large dose of hormone required is a disadvantage, and it is also important to know the time of ovulation to avoid unnecessary medication. Even so, the method would be invaluable for use in emergencies.

Male Pills. At present there are no satisfactory new methods for controlling male fertility, although attempts to develop them are being made. Spermatozoa are produced continuously throughout most of life, under the control of the two pituitary hormones that we described earlier. Steroid hormones will suppress the production of F.S.H. and L.H., just as in the female. But this leads to a reduction in the secretion of androgens by the testis, so reducing sexual drive, and there can also be feminizing effects in men. Steroids have, therefore, proved unacceptable so far. Various drugs inhibit spermatogenesis by a direct action on the testis, and do not impair libido. But these compounds were found to have unexpected and unpleasant side-effects in combination with alcohol, and their use has had to be abandoned.

Antibodies and Fertility. Immunological methods for controlling fertility could be highly acceptable in some circumstances. Antibodies which agglutinate or inactivate spermatozoa can be produced experimentally, either in males or females, and some men are naturally sterile because they produce antibodies which agglutinate their own spermatozoa. But lack of knowledge about the antibodies or their movement into the male and female reproductive tracts has hampered the development of this approach.

Outlook. In recent years, research and development into the production of new contraceptive methods have followed the advances in basic knowledge of reproductive physiology. This trend seems certain to accelerate. So far, the Pincus pill is the only product developed from basic knowledge that is in commercial use. It has been accepted on a very large scale in diverse countries, and its effect on population growth and family planning could soon be considerable. But today's pill is likely soon to be superseded by more acceptable methods, perhaps even some which confer permanent infertility until their action is deliberately reversed.*

With such methods, intercourse will be completely freed from conception. The dissemination of new methods is likely to be more rapid than in the past, for both the growth of family planning movements in Western countries and their spread into other countries in the last decade has been unprecedented. The widespread application of newer methods will be bound to affect social behaviour as much as family planning. Changes in social attitudes to family size and family spacing over future years could be considerable and widespread.

*Pills containing more than 50 mcg. oestrogen have now been withdrawn from use in the U.K. to minimize the risk of thrombo-embolism. The use of the low-dose oral, chlorinadinone acetate, has also been interrupted since the discovery of breast nodules in bitches given this form of medication.

Family Limitation Programmes in Various Countries

Colin M. Stewart

Introduction

During the years after the Second World War there was a growing awareness in many parts of the world of the problems being created by unplanned and uncontrolled population growth in the developing countries, but there was no concerted international action by governments towards finding a solution to these problems. However, a few countries acted individually to determine population policies and to make their people aware of the need for family limitation and provide the facilities whereby this limitation might be achieved. Furthermore, in many countries where the government did not take the lead, voluntary family planning associations were formed, with outside help, to which the government often gave financial assistance and which in many cases later provided the nucleus of the government's own family planning arrangements.

But however important has been the part played by these voluntary associations – and it has been and still is a very important part – it is probably only when governments themselves take the reins and make the campaign nationwide that sufficient impact can be made to achieve the drastic fall in the birth-rate necessary to halt or to effect a sizeable reduction in population growth.

A significant step forward was taken in the international field when the Secretary General of the United Nations, on Human Rights Day 10 December 1966, issued a Declaration on Population, developed on the initiative of the Chairman of the Board of the Population Council in New York, and signed by the heads of state of twelve countries. A year later, a further eighteen signatures were added to the same Declaration which described briefly the problem of unplanned population growth and then asserted:

As Heads of Governments actively concerned with the population problem we share these convictions:

We believe that the population problem must be recognized as a principal element in long-range national planning if governments are to achieve their economic goals and fulfil the aspirations of their people.

We believe that the great majority of parents desire to have the knowledge and the means to plan their families; that the opportunity to decide the number and spacing of children is a basic human right.

We believe that lasting and meaningful peace will depend to a considerable measure upon how the challenge of population growth is met.

We believe the objective of family planning is the enrichment of human life, not its restriction; that family planning, by assuring greater opportunity to each person, frees man to attain his individual dignity and reach his full potential.

Recognizing that family planning is in the vital interest of both the nation and family, we, the undersigned, earnestly hope that leaders around the world will share our views and join with us in this great challenge for the well-being and happiness of people everywhere.

A list of the 30 countries (grouped geographically) is interesting: Australia, New Zealand, the U.S.A., Barbados, Trinidad and Tobago, Colombia, the Dominican Republic, Norway, Sweden, Finland, Denmark, the Netherlands, the U.K., Yugoslavia, Morocco, Tunisia, the United Arab Republic, Jordan, Iran, Ghana, India, Pakistan, Nepal, Malaysia, Singapore, Thailand, Indonesia, South Korea, Japan, the Philippines. The main groups of countries which do not appear in this list are those with communist governments (these countries do not themselves face problems of population growth), those in Latin America (which *do* have such problems but where there are religious objections to commitment to overt policies of family limitation), countries in central and southern Europe (which do *not* face enormous problems of population growth but some of which do have religious objections to family limitation) and countries in Africa south of the Sahara. When we come to examine family limitation programmes it is not surprising, therefore, that to a large extent we find ourselves dealing with countries which have participated in the above declaration.

Up-to-date information on the formation of new national family planning programmes, and on the evaluation of the results of those at present in operation is not very easily come by. Papers by individuals are contributed to international conferences such as the United Nations World Population Conference held in Belgrade in 1965, and the Conference of the International Union for the Scientific Study of Population held in Sydney in 1967 (which concentrated on countries in the E.C.A.F.E. region), and most of these papers are subsequently published. However, perhaps the most important source providing continuous up-to-date information on this subject is to be found in the *Studies in Family Planning* published several times a year by the Population Council in New York. The Population Council (which, as mentioned earlier, provided the initiative for the Declaration on Population) is a foundation established in 1952 for scientific training and study in population matters. It endeavours to advance knowledge in the broad field of population by fostering research, training and technical consultation and assistance in the social and bio-medical sciences. The writer of the present article wishes to acknowledge that a good deal of the information on which it is based comes from these *Studies in Family Planning*.

These *Studies* are, however, only a by-product of the considerable amount of work done by the Population Council in the family planning field, in initiating, supporting and cooperating in ventures in many countries. To describe, or even to list all these activities would be a lengthy task, but perhaps two of those most recent – which are very different in form – might be mentioned.

Recognizing the great need throughout the world for energetic programmes of information and education on family planning and development of attitudes favourable to small families where at present it is the custom to have large families, the Council recently authorized the Disney studios to prepare a 10 minute colour cartoon, featuring Donald Duck, dealing with the desirability of having small families. The animated cartoon is one of the most effective materials for mass exposure, and Disney cartoons in particular are familiar and popular all over the world, so it is reasonable to expect this imaginative project to have a considerable impact. The film is entitled 'Family Planning' and will be available in at least twenty different languages.

It has long been accepted that one of the most effective points at which family planning measures may be applied is at maternity hospitals. It is there that one can focus attention on young women of childbearing age at a time when they have just given birth to a child and are therefore most receptive to advice on family planning for the future. In order to demonstrate and evaluate the effectiveness of postpartum family planning programmes, the Population Council arranged in 1966 for a co-ordinated programme to be carried out simultaneously in 25 hospitals in 19 cities in 14 different countries. Only one year's results have so far been reported, but in that period about 100,000 women accepted supplies of contraceptive pills (39 per cent) or were fitted with intra-uterine devices (51 per cent) or were sterilized (10 per cent), and in the year following they gave birth to 8,000 children against an estimated probable number of 40,000 if they had not accepted help. If this pattern of success could be repeated in an expanded programme covering perhaps a hundred times as many hospitals, the reduction in the number of births would make a significant contribution to limiting world population growth.

The first country to embark upon a nationally administered family planning programme was India, in 1951. Since then, India has been joined by others, mainly in Asia, and such information as is readily available concerning these plans, their implementation and their success, is described briefly below.

India

The first national five-year plan for India, which covered the period 1951–6, included provision for a number of studies to provide the basic information for the planning of a programme for limiting population growth, and a few experimental projects were established based on the rhythm method of avoiding conception. In the second five-year plan, a beginning was made on a nation-wide programme by setting up a family planning organization and a few training centres; interest in family planning was pro-moted through mass education media and services were provided through clinics and hospitals. The programme for contraception made very slow progress, however, and it was only through sterilization that much progress was made at all, following government approval in 1958 of sterilization as an acceptable method of family planning. In the first 10 years from 1951 to 1961 progress in the family planning field for the country as a whole was barely perceptible; the total population increased from 360,000,000 to 439,000,000, and the number of births each year had also continued to increase steadily.

The difficulties which faced, and which still face, the Indian nation are enormous. Even if satisfactory means can be found for educating a largely illiterate population to the acceptance and practice of family limitation, the physical and financial problems faced in reaching a population of over 400,000,000 are formidable indeed. While the first 10 years of family planning in India had made a beginning, it had done little more than scratch the surface of the problem. This was recognized by the Government, and the third five-year plan stepped up the programme. The budget allocated more than ten times as much money as in the previous five-year plan, and some progress was made towards creating a favourable climate for the acceptance of family planning and for overcoming apathy. Apart from sterilization, the main plank of the programme was the use of condoms, but this was expensive and required a vast network of distribution centres to produce any real impact on overall fertility.

The arrival of intra-uterine devices (I.U.D.s) on the scene in

India in 1965 changed matters considerably. Because of the great clinical and administrative advantages of this method over sterilization, an effective mass programme now seemed feasible, and the Government acted to seize the new opportunity. A Special Committee was formed 'to review what additions and changes were necessary as a result of the greatly altered situation . . .' A Family Planning Committee was set up at Cabinet level and the Ministry of Health was renamed the Ministry of Health and Family Planning. The family planning programme was reorganized with the District as the pivotal point and the whole operation made more purposeful and effective than hitherto. In the fourth five-year plan (1966–71) the budget allocation for family planning was again increased considerably to approximately 200,000,000 U.S. dollars.

To put this figure in its proper perspective, the total population of India in 1966 was about 500,000,000, so the budget allocation works out at about 40 cents per head, or 8 cents per year. (The money will go a lot further than this, of course, because the greater part of the population are not prospective users of contraceptives.) Over the five years 1966–71, 20,000,000 I.U.D. insertions are planned, 5,000,000 vasectomies (sterilization of the male) and it is hoped to have 10,000,000 effective users of traditional contraceptives. It is hoped by continuing these methods, to reduce the birth-rate from about 40 per thousand total population to 25 per thousand by the year 1975, which by then will mean a reduction of about 9,000,000 births a year. The impact of this programme on the national birth-rate is as yet fairly small, but in those areas where the family planning activities have been most intensive, cuts in the birth-rate of between 10 and 20 per cent have been reported, and it has been officially estimated that about 1,200,000 births were prevented in 1967. At last it seems that the Indian family planning programme has gained some of the momentum which is essential if it is to have the impact necessary on the rate of growth of its already large population.

Pakistan

In Pakistan, the family planning programme was drawn up in 1960 and, having passed through the preliminary stages, reached the stage of implementation as part of the national five-year plan for 1965–70. The target is to make family planning services available to all fertile couples in Pakistan (estimated to number about 20,000,000 out of a total population of 116,000,000) and to reduce the birth-rate from 50 per thousand to 45 per thousand by 1970, with further reductions in later years. The State has budgeted about 12 cents a head during each of the five years and a Central Family Planning Council has been established with the Minister of Health as Chairman and the appointment of a Commissioner of Family Planning to run the organization.

Implementation of the plan is concentrated on the I.U.D. and on conventional contraceptives, principally condoms and foam tablets, but studies of acceptability are being made concerning the oral pill. By September 1967, two years after the programme was launched, a total of over 1,000,000 I.U.D. insertions and about 100,000 vasectomies had been carried out, and the monthly sales of conventional contraceptives exceeded 13,000,000, an impressive level of acceptance of the family planning programme.

While precise figures are not available by which the success of these arrangements could be measured, reports suggest that they are having the planned effect in bringing down the birth-rate.

South Korea

The third Asian country, after India and Pakistan, to organize a national family planning programme was South Korea, and in that country of about 30,000,000 people the progress has been rapid and tangible results can be observed. Things did not really get moving until 1963 when there was an energetic 'mass enlightenment' campaign which resulted in more than 1,000,000 couples registering their interest in family planning and accepting a trial supply of condoms or foam tablets. Tests were also started on I.U.D.s.

In 1964 the main staffing of the Korean national programme began and the target for 1965 was 200,000 I.U.D. insertions, 300,000 users of traditional contraceptives (of which the condom was the most popular) and 20,000 vasectomies, a total of over 500,000 active participants in the family planning programme. The 1965 target was not in fact reached, partly as a result of shortage of foreign currency for the importation of contraceptives; but Korea now manufactures all its own supplies, and even exports some.

The target for 1966 was 400,000 I.U.D. insertions, 20,000 vasectomies, and 150,000 (half the 1965 target) users of condoms, etc., and the actual achievement was very close to this target. By the end of 1967 the cumulative total number of I.U.D. insertions had reached 1,000,000 and by the end of 1971 it is hoped that there will have been in all 1,800,000 I.U.D. insertions (of which perhaps 1,000,000 will still be in place) and 150,000 vasectomies, and 150,000 persons will be using condoms, etc., making a total of 1,300,000 participating in the family planning programme at that time. This will represent a substantial proportion of the young married persons who are the major contributors to the country's births, and it is hoped that the birth-rate in 1971 will thus be reduced to about 30 per thousand population from the 1962 figure of about 40 per thousand. Accurate birth-rate statistics are not available for South Korea, but the Planning Board estimated that by the end of 1966 the birth-rate had already fallen to about 35 per thousand, a reduction of perhaps 150,000 births a year.

Concern is felt at the relatively high proportion of cases where an I.U.D. is not retained, for one reason or another, and an alternative method of contraception is being sought for such cases. Field studies are being carried out with the prospect of the oral pill becoming the second line of defence but, although the cost of these pills has fallen drastically, it can still be a sizeable item in the budget of a developing country. Nevertheless, the expenditure on the whole family planning programme in South

Korea is only about 5 cents per head of the population compared with 8 cents in India and 12 cents in Pakistan and it appears to be getting a very good return from its investment in family planning compared with these two much larger countries.

Taiwan

The position in Taiwan, with a total population of about 13,000,000, is somewhat similar to that in South Korea, although governmental support in funds and facilities is given without any formal declaration of official policy. The birth-rate had already fallen from about 45 per thousand in 1955 to 33 per thousand in 1965, the first full year of the nation-wide family planning programme, and the aim of the programme was to continue the existing downward trend to about 20 per thousand by 1973. The principal method in use is the I.U.D. and by the end of 1967 there had been 370,000 insertions; the June 1969 target is for a total of 600,000.

The drop in the cost of the oral pill has opened up new possibilities of this method as an alternative. Commercial sales of pills have risen, showing that the method is gaining popularity, and pills can now be supplied through governmental channels, primarily for women who cannot retain an I.U.D. supplied under the family planning programme. One of the manufacturers has sent to Taiwan 250,000 cycles of pills so that a large-scale experiment might be conducted.

In Taiwan there are few large maternity hospitals, so that the operation of the kind of postpartum programme described earlier in this article is not possible. However, a substitute programme of writing to every woman who has recently registered a birth has been in operation and, having produced a significant return at very low cost, is being expanded. It is necessary, of course, for the population of a country to be literate for this technique to be used.

Mainland China

Estimates of the population of this vast nation usually arrive at an answer over 700,000,000, so its importance in the field of world population is pre-eminent. Information on policy and statistics on population and family planning is not, however, readily available. Premier Chou En-lai is reported as having stated in 1964:

We do believe in planned parenthood, but it is not easy to introduce all at once in China and it is more difficult to achieve in rural areas, where most of our people live, than in the cities. The first thing is to encourage late marriages . . .

Articles in the Chinese Press have stressed the advisability of late marriages for both men and women, and have suggested that families should be limited to 2, or at the most 3 children. If both 'recommendations' are followed by the population at large, this should prevent any catastrophic further increase in numbers, and in view of the effectiveness of the propaganda media in China, who can doubt that these recommendations *will* be followed? All but the most optimistic forecasts, however, on deferment of age at marriage and strict limitation of families, estimate that the population will exceed 1,000,000,000 by the end of the present century.

Malaysia

The national family planning programme in Malaysia is of fairly recent origin. The Family Planning Act became law only in June 1966 and established the National Family Planning Board with the objectives of formulating policy and directing and coordinating family planning activities. This includes the training of personnel; conducting research on medical and biological methods relating to family planning; the promotion of studies and research on the interrelationship between social, cultural, economic and population changes and on fertility and maternity patterns in the country; and setting up a system for assessing from time to time the effectiveness of the programme and the progress made towards the attainment of national objectives. The Malaysian Government also pays an annual grant to the voluntary

Malaysian Federation of Family Planning Associations which have been active, in some States, since 1953, and the Board acts in cooperation with these Associations. For example, the Board's activities in the cities are primarily through the maternity hospitals and patients are frequently referred to the Association clinic nearest their home for advice and supplies.

The clinical programme of the Board began in May 1967, after suitable qualified staff had been recruited, and although it is gaining momentum in both expansion of services and the numbers of women accepting contraceptives, at the time of writing (1968) it is still too early to see any significant result in the crude birth-rate. The birth-rate in Malaysia has, however, already fallen from 46 per thousand in 1957 to 37 per thousand in 1966 due, it is thought, in part to an increase in the average age at marriage and in part to deliberate child spacing and limitation of family size by various means. These means include fairly high commercial sales of pills as well as other means and it is interesting to note that it is the pill, rather than I.U.D. as in many other developing countries, which is used in the great majority of cases (90 per cent of new patients choose the pill). This preference is no doubt due in large part to previous knowledge of, if not actual use, of this method.

Hong Kong and Singapore

There is a great deal of similarity between Hong Kong and Singapore. Both are small islands with expanding populations, but they are relatively compact communities and do not have, like some large Asian countries, numerous small villages remote from urban areas and from modern influences. Both have active voluntary family planning associations whose activities have resulted in a steady decline in the birth-rate in recent years. These associations received government subsidies and support and, in 1965–6 in Singapore, the government took over responsibility for family planning by setting up the Singapore Family Planning and Population Board charged with the responsibility for implementing a five-year plan aimed at teaching 180,000 women (nearly one-tenth of the island's total population, and thus a major part of the female population of childbearing age).

In addition to conventional contraceptives, both islands have embarked on extensive programmes for the insertion of I.U.D.s. In Hong Kong, by the end of 1965, about 50,000 insertions had been made; in Singapore, the government programme started in 1966 and figures are not readily available. It has also been estimated that, in 1967, the number of women using oral contraceptives was over 50,000 in Hong Kong and over 70,000 in Singapore, which are very significant figures in relation to the sizes of the total populations and to the other forms of contraceptives available and in use.

The crude birth-rate in Hong Kong has fallen from 36 per thousand in 1960 to 25 per thousand in 1966, and in Singapore over the same period from 39 to 29. This is an excellent result and there are prospects that the decline will continue in both communities although the changing age distribution of the population may make it difficult to maintain.

Japan

The years since the Second World War have seen a truly remarkable decline in the birth-rate in Japan. Some decline had occurred in the years before the war, associated probably with the growing industrialization of the country, but the rate was still high, about 30 per thousand population, and in the years immediately after the war, was even higher at 34 per thousand. Grave concern was voiced by many experts and social leaders about the country's rapidly growing population and the prospects of overpopulation. Public forums were held frequently and there was sensational reporting on the radio and in the press. Confronted with extreme difficulties in their daily life in the aftermath of war, the Japanese people as a whole reacted strongly in favour of birth control and resorted to abortion on a growing scale. When in 1948 the Eugenic Protection Law was passed, making induced abortion legal, this was to a very large extent bringing out into the open and consequently making much safer (and, as it turned out, much more frequent) a practice which had already become well established but which, because it was practised clandestinely, exposed the women concerned to a considerable risk of harmful effects.

In the years immediately following the passing of the 1948 Act the number of induced abortions reported to the authorities rose steadily and the number of live births registered fell equally steadily. Between 1949 and 1955, the total of the two together remained at roughly 2,900,000, but while abortions rose from 200,000 to 1,200,000, live births fell from 2,700,000 to 1,700,000. These figures provide striking evidence of the rapid decline in births in Japan, and relate the decline directly to legalized abortion following the passing of the 1948 Act.

The government of Japan was aware of this trend in the number of abortions and in 1952 the Ministry of Health and Welfare issued an official instruction to all prefectures urging them to make efforts to promote contraception throughout the country, it being hoped that this would take the place of the interruption of pregnancy by induced abortion which, even under clinical conditions, could not invariably be carried out without damaging the mother's health. In spite of this, the number of induced abortions remained high and did not fall below 1,000,000 until 1962. Current surveys show that more than half of married couples in Japan now use contraceptives, almost entirely of the conventional kind.

The total population of Japan is now about 100,000,000 and the birth rate has fallen to about 17 per thousand. For about 10 years, the number of births has been about 1,600,000 or 1,700,000 and if – and it is a big 'if' – it can be held at this level, the total population of Japan in the long term will be about 70 times this number of births, or perhaps 120,000,000, which would be a very modest increase on the present total of 100,000,000.

Turkey

For many years Turkey had an anti-contraceptive law, but in spite of this the Economic Planning Board began working in the early 1960s towards legislative changes and programme planning. This far-sightedness saved valuable time when government policy changed. In early 1965 Turkey repealed the old laws forbidding abortion, sterilization and the importation and sale of contraceptives or the dissemination of information about them; a Family Planning Law was passed to implement a national programme through the Ministry of Health and Social Assistance, with cooperation from the Army and other government agencies.

Popular approval of contraception and of government involvement in a national programme had been clearly established beforehand by a sample survey covering more than 5,000 married persons in 240 villages and 70 large centres of population. The wishes of the Turkish people were thus made clear and in 1965 the government responded by becoming one of the earliest to embark on a national programme of family planning, but it is still too early to look for evidence of progress in terms of a reduction in births.

Africa

In 1964 Tunisia became the first North African country to declare a national family planning programme. Pilot studies have been made and an initial I.U.D. experiment. The target announced is for one I.U.D. insertion a year for every 12 women of child-bearing age, in the hope of reducing the birth-rate by one-quarter in 5 years. In addition, a law has been passed permitting abortion for women who already have more than 4 children.

In the United Arab Republic, a nation of 30,000,000 people, a family programme has begun under the direction of the Supreme Council for Family Planning created by the government in November 1965. A large number of maternity and child welfare clinics offer advice and services. Large-scale manufacture of oral pills and I.U.D.s is going ahead within the U.A.R. and these are distributed free of charge.

In 1965 the government of Kenya invited a team of experts to study population problems in that country and to make recommendations on the ideal rate of growth and how to attain that rate, including recommendations on the organization and financing of a family planning programme. The experts reported in August 1965, recommending that surveys should be carried out to determine people's knowledge, attitudes and practices regarding family planning. They recommended that the main instrument in the programme should be the insertion of I.U.D.s; pilot studies should therefore be undertaken to determine the suitability and acceptability of I.U.D.s to the people of Kenya. The experts considered that it might be possible to implement a programme which would reduce the birth-rate by as much as one-half in 10–15 years.

In Ghana, independent surveys have already shown public attitudes which are consistent with the regulation of fertility, and it is thought that this attitude is probably typical of many other central African countries, but in none of them has a family planning programme yet been implemented.

Latin America

There are no advanced government programmes for family planning in this area, although with a combined total population of over 250,000,000 increasing at a rate of about 3 per cent per year there is an obvious need for it. Voluntary associations are at work, however, and four of the twenty-five hospitals participating in the international postpartum family planning programme mentioned above are in this region. It is estimated that over 2,000,000 women are currently using oral contraceptive pills, notably in Argentina, Brazil and Mexico, and this will be making some impact, even if not a very dramatic one. In Chile, a voluntary National Committee is officially backed by the National Health Service, which contributes such key personnel as doctors, nurses and midwives. Almost all Santiago public hospitals offer birth-control supplies and I.U.D. research is being carried out.

Although statistics relating to the number of illegal abortions are, for obvious reasons, lacking or at best unreliable, the incidence is thought to be high and is resulting in widespread maternal deaths and ill health. While the incidence is not sufficiently high to lower the birth-rate, nevertheless its adverse effects are sufficiently widespread to provide an important stimulus to the liberalization of attitudes towards contraception.

Developed countries

In developed countries generally, the average family size and the rate of population increase have fallen to acceptable levels as a result of the voluntary limitation of families by a large proportion of the population, so that there is no pressing national need for programmes of family limitation. National services can therefore be directed towards providing assistance for infertile women desiring children and to providing facilities which would make *every* child born a wanted child.

In the United Kingdom, it has long been possible to obtain help under the National Health Service in cases of infertility, but it is only since June 1967, with the passing of the National Health Service (Family Planning) Act 1967, that local health authorities have been able to provide contraceptive advice and appliances (not necessarily free of charge), and since October 1967, under the Abortion Act 1967, that the medical termination of pregnancy has been permissible in certain specified circumstances.

In France as long ago as 1920 a law was passed forbidding the sale of contraceptives but this was changed in 1967 when the sale of contraceptives on medical prescription was made permissible to anyone over the age of 18. Somewhat paradoxically, the advertising of contraceptives remains forbidden and subject to even heavier penalties than before.

Generally speaking, even in those countries where contraception is officially frowned on, perhaps on religious grounds, there is sufficient knowledge of and availability of means of birth control. The legalization of abortion is quite another matter, however, and many countries set their faces firmly against its being permitted in any circumstances whatsoever. Communist countries have generally been liberal in their attitude and have permitted abortion in a wide variety of circumstances, but in

East Germany and very recently in certain other east European countries, worries about the possibility of population decline have caused a reversal of this attitude.

Conclusion

Undoubtedly the above description of family planning programmes is incomplete, both from the omission of recent developments in the countries mentioned, and from the exclusion altogether of some countries in which progress in family limitation is being made. The picture for the world as a whole is nevertheless fairly clear.

To say the least, it is highly desirable that a pattern of small families should very quickly become established in the developing countries. It would be very imprudent to wait for this to happen slowly as industrial development progresses. It is therefore necessary for the peoples of the developing countries, first to be motivated to a desire to limit their families, and secondly to have the means whereby this desire can be met.

In Japan, a country already industrialized, the desire was there soon after the War, the method chosen without inhibition by the Japanese people was abortion, and the purpose was achieved very quickly, although abortion as the main method is now giving way to contraception.

In countries of the Far East, attitudes have rapidly become favourable to family limitation and, with the appearance of relatively cheap contraceptives like the I.U.D. and the oral pill, the means is now available and rapid progress is being made.

In countries like India and Pakistan, motivation towards family limitation is spreading much more slowly, although with growing vigour, but the relatively cheap devices now available – and still being developed – suggest that tangible progress is likely to be made in the foreseeable future.

In Latin America and Africa the prospects are less clear, but the greater the progress in the rest of the world, the brighter the prospects that similar progress will subsequently be made in these regions.

Bibliography

REFERENCES

Papers contributed to the Sydney Conference of the International Union for the Scientific Study of Population, August 1967.

Proceedings of the World Population Conference (United Nations), Belgrade, 30 August–10 September 1965.

Studies in Family Planning, The Population Council, New York. Published by the International Planned Parenthood Federation, London: *World Survey (1) Factors Affecting the Work of Family Planning Associations*, September 1966; *World Survey (2) Focus on Latin America*, January 1967; *Directory of Selected Training Facilities in Family Planning and Allied Subjects*, March 1967; *Family Planning in Five Continents*, June 1968.

The Economic and Social Implications of Population Control

Colin Clark

A fertile married couple, living together and making no attempt to restrict conception, and with the mother lactating, produce on the average, while their fertility lasts, 0·4 offspring per year, i.e. there is an average interval between births of $2\frac{1}{2}$ years. This average of course conceals wide individual variations. There are also wide variations in the age of onset of infertility in women. Some are infertile throughout their lives, and some conceive when nearly 50; but the average duration of fertility is probably about 20 years. This means that in a community where every girl married young, widows quickly re-married, and no restrictions were placed on conception, the average woman would have produced about 8 offspring if she had survived to the end of her reproductive period. In a primitive hunting community – the state of life for the whole human race outside the last few thousand years of our million or so years of existence on this planet – this rate of reproduction almost exactly suffices to replace the heavy mortality suffered by such communities, keeping mankind, if you like to put it that way, in a state of 'ecological equilibrium'. Population increases in such primitive hunting communities, whether calculated by archaeologists from the past, or observed by anthropologists in the present, are extremely slow, if indeed they take place at all.

This 'natural' rate of reproduction, with the reduced rates of mortality prevailing in a settled agricultural population, suffices to make some population increase possible; in a community with our standards of mortality, it would lead to a population increase of 7 per cent per year or more. Agricultural communities in Europe in the past however reduced the average completed family to 5 or 6, by social customs calling for deferment of marriage and some discouragement of the re-marriage of widows. Methods of restricting conception in marriage (probably by *coitus interruptus*, though we cannot be sure) appeared in rural France about 1780, and had probably been used earlier in some urban societies. The use of mechanical contraceptives on any extensive scale had to await the discovery of the technology of vulcanizing rubber in 1843.

The study of the economic and social 'implications' of population control (by all methods, including deferment of marriage) requires us to consider first its causes, then its consequences.

It is customary to say that the principal cause of family limitation is 'higher standards of living'. No scientist should tolerate such an expression, under any circumstances. In the first place, the phrase 'standard of living' is hopelessly ambiguous. People sometimes use it to describe what people think they ought to get, sometimes what they actually do get, two very different meanings. Some writers are so gloriously muddled that they use the phrase with its two opposed meanings in the course of the same text.

What people think that they ought to get is not an object capable of direct measurement, though economists and sociologists may be able to obtain some indirect information on the subject. What they are actually receiving is generally capable of measurement, though we only darken counsel by trying to amalgamate it all into a single measure. We must examine separately income, nature of occupation, education and other variables. The economic variable which is often unprecisely described as 'standard of living' should be called 'real income'. (The adjective 'real' indicates that we have taken into account differences in prices, as well as the face values of incomes.)

The analysis of the inter-correlated effects of income, occupation and education on size of family has proved to be, in spite of the abundance of information, an exceptionally complex task, and no simple conclusions are to be drawn.

But there is another sociological variable which we have not yet considered, which probably plays a larger part than any other in determining family size, and hence rate of population growth. This is the distinction between the 'nuclear family' and the 'extended family'. The nuclear family, which is customary in the economically advanced countries, consists solely of husband, wife and dependent children. Such families, even though enjoying a level of real income far above that of their predecessors, or of the rest of the world, nevertheless find the raising of a large number of children very difficult, for several reasons. The first is that in such communities there is likely to be a great deal of what is best described by the emotionally neutral word 'emulation' (the colloquial phrase for which is 'keeping up with the Joneses'); which is less likely to be found in simpler societies. Secondly, although current income may be high, the father is bound to feel considerable anxiety about unforeseen contingencies, illness, unemployment, etc., in the case of which the family would have to depend on its own accumulated resources, with little help from outside. Thirdly, the mother is concerned with the long hours of work in providing and watching the children, again being able to expect little or no help from outside. In the extended family, whether in Africa or in Asia today, or among our own ancestors, things are very different. There will be grandparents and uncles and aunts and cousins and others about who will give both economic and child-minding help if required. At present the African tribe (or, for that matter, the Scottish clan of not so very long ago) could almost be described as one large extended family.

There is a price to be paid for this. Men living in an extended family, knowing that they are not solely responsible for the welfare of their children, and at the same time that, if successful, they will probably have to share their earnings with a number of relatives to whom they are not very closely attached, are likely to work much less energetically than men living in nuclear families. The advent of the nuclear family has done a great deal to promote the creation of wealth in modern Europe and North America, and at the same time, to discourage the creation of children. These two consequences both spring from this one cause. It is erroneous to say that it is the wealth itself which discourages the birth of children.

In France in the 1890s family limitation had already been in operation for over a century, and the effects on France's rate of population growth, in comparison with that of neighbouring countries, were already clearly apparent, and were giving concern to French soldiers and statesmen. It was against this background that Arsène Dumont pioneered the sociological study of family limitation. His object was to discourage it. France at that time was the only country in the world upholding the republican and atheistic principles which he valued, and was clearly falling behind in the world power race. If only he could persuade his fellow countrymen to bring up larger families, this would serve to 'keep the men out of the taverns and the girls out of the churches'. Dumont had no success in this direction. But his sociological analyses were very valuable. He coined the interesting phrase 'social capillarity'. If a tube is thrust vertically through the surface of a fluid, the fluid will rise in the tube by capillary action; and the narrower the tube, the greater the rise. So it is with families; those who limit their numbers will accumulate more capital to enable their sons to succeed better in business. In the case of civil servants (Dumont's own profession) what matters is not the accumulation of capital, but ability to spend money in going to the right social gatherings, so that one is noticed, and achieves promotion. (Still true today?) Interesting exceptions to this rule were the linguistic minorities (Bretons, Basques, etc.), who had little prospect of economic or social advancement, and who had much larger families than their French-speaking neighbours. Dumont's generalization is still found to be widely true of linguistic and religious minorities all over the world.

French concern with population problems has continued, and France is now the principal centre of demographic research. The recently retired Director of the National Institute of Demographic Research in Paris, Alfred Sauvy, stated the issue in a striking manner. 'Would the size of family in the Middle Ages still have been high', he asked, 'if each peasant had been able to cherish the hope of some day becoming a *seigneur*, or of his son becoming one, if he were able to concentrate all his efforts on giving one son a good education?' The prospects, or lack of them, of social and economic advancement, play a big part in determining the size of family. Under an extended family system these prospects, so far as individual parents are concerned, are always small; though this is also true of a number of nuclear-family societies.

But now let us look at the question from the point of view of the extended family, presuming, as is usually the case, that it is engaged in peasant agriculture. Such a family will see a child, subject to a short period of waiting, as an economic asset. By the time it has reached the age of 7, the work which it will do on the farm or in the household will exceed the cost of its keep. And it is not only in the poorest peasant societies that this is the case. In 1837, when Parliament was examining the question of providing schools in Australia, a witness told the Select Committee that 'even at six years of age, the services of children become valuable, and with many of the lower classes of settler this might operate against their wish to send them to school'. What had hitherto been essential features of extended-family life were, in nineteenth-century Europe and North America, removed by the combined effects of legislation and social custom, namely by the obligation to send children to school, and by the discouragement or prohibition of child labour. In most of Asia, Africa and Latin America these changes have not yet come about – nor are they likely to do so in the near future.

In India, and in many other countries with a monsoonal climate, farm families experience a good deal of enforced idleness during the long dry season. But this does not invalidate their need for child labour – rather the reverse. When the rain does come, enforced idleness gives way to acute labour shortage. Under these circumstances the help of children is urgently necessary for the farm economy.

There is another essential difference between their type of society and ours, so important that few people ever notice it. We take it for granted that, if we are in real trouble, public authority will at least save us from starvation, and indeed probably do substantially more than that. We and our ancestors have been able to live under this rule for several centuries now, and the assumption has become second nature to us. But this is far from being true in Asia, Africa or Latin America. However humane the authorities may be, they know perfectly well that the offer of any kind of National Assistance, on however meagre a scale, would immediately be swamped by applicants. The grim truth is that, in these large areas of the world, if you are in trouble you have only your family to turn to. If you have no family, there is nothing to do but to go out and beg in the street, and quite probably you will literally starve. This state of affairs creates an immensely strong urge in parents to beget children, who will give them some help in age or infirmity. Those who are so urgently telling the Indians not to have children might at least offer to provide them with some form of alternative social security, which their own government has not done yet.

In Africa, the extended family, and with it the tendency to bring up as many children as possible, is almost universal. The average size of family in Africa however is substantially lower than elsewhere in the world, for medical reasons not yet fully understood. There may be some inherited infertility; but widespread venereal disease is a more probable explanation. In Asia the extended family is almost universal among Hindus, except for the urbanized minority; but in other parts of Asia, and also among low-caste Hindus, many of the poor live in nuclear families. In this case, however, there is little if any indication of the nuclear families being less reproductive than the extended families. The situation in Latin America appears to be intermediate between that of Africa and of Asia.

We must indeed be aware that the major sociological division of the world is between the nuclear-family and the extended-family societies. With this in mind, we turn to the lesser issue of the social and economic factors affecting family size in nuclear-family societies such as our own. Most people have unduly simplified ideas on this subject. 'The rich get richer and the poor get children' was the way in which the Victorians expressed it.

In their own time this was more or less true. But now that we are accumulating enough information to give us some historical perspective, we will probably have to conclude that the late nineteenth and early twentieth centuries constituted a sandwich between the periods before and after, in which the wealthy and educated were *more* reproductive than the poor.

For peasant societies, whether in Asia now or in Europe in the past, we have clear evidence of such a relationship. The control, of course, is largely exercised by age at marriage. The daughters of the wealthier families have dowries and marry earlier than the daughters of poor families. This also appears to have been true of urban societies in the past.

In the modern world, the first signs of a change in tendency were observed in Sweden, a country where family limitation had been extensively practised already, as early as 1930. By this time, almost all families in Sweden were practising family limitation. But the educated were found to be practising it to a somewhat less extent than the uneducated. Throughout Europe and North America the evidence is the same – most of the former fertility differentials are now disappearing, whether due to income, educational, occupational, religious or urban-rural differences. In France, a country of generally low fertility, there are many (not all) rural areas, particularly in the south, whose fertility has long been below that of the industrial areas. Religious differences persist, but to a much less extent than before, particularly in the large cities. Education of the mother has more effect than education of the father. Information from the United States Census of 1960 shows that the family is reduced by 0·04 offspring on the average for each extra year of education above the minimum received by the father, by 0·08 for each extra year received by the mother.

We turn now to the consequences of population control. The first issue that we should consider is that of possible genetic consequences. Those of us who date back to the 1920s will remember the great days of the Eugenics Society, which included a number of distinguished scientists among its members, complaining that the genetic quality of the nation was deteriorating because (at that time) family limitation was substantially practised by the wealthy and educated, much less by the rest of the community, hardly at all by the unskilled. The Eugenists however were never very clear about how they proposed to persuade what they regarded as the superior stocks to breed more, except by advocating a reduction of taxation, which at that time in any case was very low in comparison with the present. Their case naturally weakened as the practice of family limitation rapidly spread to almost all sections of the community. But, in addition, it became clear that to identify the possession of wealth or education with genetic superiority was entirely unscientific, indeed an insufferable piece of social conceit. Likewise the claim that there was an abundance of genetic defects, particularly hereditary mental deficiency, among the poor and unskilled, proved to be a prejudice quite incapable of substantiation by scientific evidence.

It is indeed only quite recently that any substantial stock of information on human genetics has become available – we now have accurate knowledge of quite a large number of genetically transmitted defects, most of them fortunately rare. This knowledge leads to important conclusions, such as the desirability of avoiding first-cousin marriages. But it seems to have no relation to the question of family limitation.

There should be one consequence of family limitation which, on the face of it, should hardly need discussion, namely that the offspring of small families should be more likely to secure economic and social advancement than the offspring of large families. But it has proved very difficult to subject this simple generalization to accurate statistical testing. A large-scale study carried out in France by Bresard showed that it was true in general, to a moderate degree, but with a striking exception at the top of the social scale, in respect of the sons of professional men and business proprietors. Among these, the sons born in the larger families actually received *more* education than those born in smaller families, and, perhaps under the stimulus of necessity, tended to be more successful in their subsequent careers.

To some extent also we can make these social comparisons international. It may be significant that one of the highest rates of social mobility (i.e. opportunity for sons of poorer families to obtain social and economic advancement) in the world now appears to prevail in Japan, a country which has carried family limitation to the point where the present generation is failing, by a substantial margin, to replace itself. In the United States, once described as 'the land of opportunity', it is true that free secondary education is available to all, but substantial fees have to be paid for higher education. There is also considerable social and economic segregation, not only of the coloured people, but also of the large Spanish-speaking community in the West, members of which rarely attain economic and social advancement.

The economics of population growth are paradoxical. The economic burden which an additional child imposes upon the individual family is immediate and obvious. But when we consider the economics of the community as a whole, and after a due period of time, population growth is nearly always found to be advantageous.

No doubt it is because of the conflict between this proposition, and the obvious burden on the individual family, which makes people find it hard to accept.

However, in an advanced industrial country, it can be seen clearly that business always finds a large and growing market advantageous. Most types of industry, transport, etc. can be better organized for a large market than for a small one. The economic term for this phenomenon is 'economies of scale', which are of very substantial importance. Indeed they account for the greater part of the higher levels of productivity and real wages in the United States, as compared with Europe. A fivefold or sixfold productivity advantage has been obtained in those American industries which work on the very largest scale, such as vehicles, timber, chemicals and electrical goods; relatively much less advantage is obtained by industries not working on so large a scale.

There is another phenomenon which has been observed in every industrial country. Certain favoured regions (in this country, the south-east and the midlands) already densely populated, appear to possess the ability of attracting to themselves further industry and population to an inordinate degree. Indeed the truth is, in such cases, that the effect of population growth is not poverty, but excessive wealth. It is true that these industrial areas of rapidly growing population suffer a number of difficulties, such as pressure on the public services, or traffic congestion, and difficulty of access to the countryside. These difficulties can be put right by good planning. But they are not signs of economic poverty.

It is in agricultural communities that the economic advantages of population growth may at first sight appear more questionable. Malthus said in 1798 that population growth, unless checked by later marriage, or by 'vice and misery', would always overtake the growth of agricultural production. When we look at what has happened in the world since 1798 – Malthus thought that Britain was over-populated already in his own time – we conclude that there must be something wrong with this highly simplified generalization. 'Ah!', exclaim the neo-Malthusians, 'what has happened has been that there were some unexpected technical improvements in agricultural productivity, and now population is growing up again to absorb them.' But closer analysis shows that this is, in most cases, the opposite of the truth – population increase generally comes first, and then, usually with great reluctance, people adopt technically more efficient methods because they have to provide for the increased population. The strongest reason for believing that things work this way round is that almost every technical improvement in agriculture involves, in its initial stages, harder and more disagreeable work than the methods previously used. Technical knowledge, in most countries, is available well ahead of the actual adoption of technical improvements.

This began a long time ago. I like to picture our ancestors in the country in the Middle Stone Age, about 5000 B.C. The population of England had risen to some 15,000, and it was quite clear that the country could not support any more, if each family was to have adequately sized hunting and fishing grounds. I envisage the wise men of the tribes holding meetings, and doing whatever then corresponded to writing letters to *The Times*, pointing out the urgent need for family limitation. Some bold spirit may have suggested emigration to Scotland, which would have been ruled out as impracticable. Some still rasher young man may have suggested trying this 'agriculture', which had recently been discovered in Egypt and Babylonia, which made it possible to feed a large population on a much smaller area, only to be told that this certainly would not work in England. However, we know what happened. Eventually, with immense reluctance, our ancestors had to give up their agreeable hunting and fishing, and take to the laborious and degrading pursuit of agriculture.

While this account is fictional, we have more precise information about the situation in America, where what is now the territory of the United States and Canada was carrying a population of about 1,000,000 at the beginning of the sixteenth century, and these people were finding the country seriously overpopulated. In their case, a much more advanced civilization, based on maize growing, was available near at hand in Mexico, and knowledge of agriculture spread northward quite rapidly.

In some parts of Europe, as sardonic critics have pointed out, agricultural methods, based upon ox-ploughs, did not change very much from the late Stone Age until the present century. But England had an agricultural revolution, if we recollect what we read in our history books about a man called Townshend who invented turnips, and so on. The actual truth is that many of the improvements in agriculture, such as the growing of turnips and lucerne (though not of course potatoes) were known in the ancient world, and neglected in medieval Europe, and restored when population growth demanded it. This theory is confirmed by the first appearance of such improvements in the most densely populated parts of Europe, such as the Low Countries and Northern Italy, reaching England much later – though even so, they did not all come in a rush in the late eighteenth century, as the traditional history books would have us believe.

In most of 'black Africa' (i.e. excluding South Africa, and the Mediterranean-African countries), and in large areas in Asia and

Latin America too, the agriculture still practised is of the most primitive and wasteful variety, consisting of cutting down and burning a patch of forest, taking 2 or 3 crops out of the soil fertilized by the ashes, and then abandoning the land again for a 15 or 20-year cycle while the trees re-grow. Under this system, only about 3 per cent of the available land is actually cultivated in any one year. It is not that Africans are ignorant of more intensive forms of agriculture – there are indeed a few isolated places in Africa whose inhabitants have been compelled by special circumstances to practise very highly intensive and productive forms of agriculture – it is that 'cut and burn' agriculture offers an easy life, with plenty of leisure. As population density increases, it becomes necessary to clear the forest in shorter rotations, crop yields decrease, and we are told of the grave hardships which the people are suffering. Eventually the time comes when they have to practise settled agriculture, which calls for much more continuous work, but which enables a much larger population to be supported from a given area of land.

Such agricultural communities are indeed suffering – in every respect except their abundant leisure – from under-population. Careful analyses have shown that, until population density rises to about 27 persons per km^2, it is impossible to drive away the wild animals and to cut the scrub which harbours the tsetse fly. Still less is it possible for such sparse communities to build the roads, water supply, schools, etc., on which more advanced societies depend.

What happened in eighteenth-century England provided a model for what was to happen, in more dramatic form, in nineteenth-century Japan. It was in the Revolution of 1868 that the young Emperor Meiji resumed power from the hereditary noblemen who had governed and kept the country in a state of stagnation for the preceding $2\frac{1}{2}$ centuries. Throughout this 'Tokugawa Period' population had been kept practically stationary, mainly by the method, as Japanese historians freely admit, of infanticide. After 1868 this suddenly came to an end, and the population began to grow. Agricultural productivity also grew, much more rapidly than population, producing sufficient food for a quickly increasing industrial population, and also enabling the farmers themselves to eat more.

One does not usually think of India in these terms. But since becoming an independent country in 1947, India has also been undergoing an agricultural revolution. It is true, to those of us who are its contemporaries, that it does not look very rapid – but if we had been actually living in late eighteenth-century England, or late nineteenth-century Japan, the pace of progress would have looked to us painfully slow. Indian population increase, at a rate anything like that which prevails now, did not begin until the 1930s. At first, agricultural production failed to keep pace with population increase, but during the 1950s and 1960s it has exceeded it, although not by the wide margin which one would have preferred to see, which would have enabled India to feed an increasing proportion of her labour force in industrial occupations. But by contrast with the stagnant previous history of Indian agriculture, changes have been rapid, including some improvement in seed, the application of substantial quantities of chemical fertilizers for the first time, and the concentration of half the land in the hands of the top 15 per cent of the largest and most productive farmers.

In Pakistan the rate of population increase is a little higher than in India. This country, after a late start, is now showing a rate of growth of agricultural productivity much higher than India's through heavy subsidization of fertilizers and encouragement of well-irrigation.

In most other Asian countries – apart from China – there is, contrary to general belief, little population pressure. In Ceylon, Burma, Malaysia, Indonesia, Thailand and the Philippines, there is abundant land, with good soil and rainfall, still lying unused. Under these circumstances, it is an observed fact that agricultural productivity does not increase. The rising population finds sufficient additional land to cultivate, by the old-fashioned low-productivity methods.

Let us conclude with some more detailed examination of the effects of population growth in more advanced countries. The evidence for 'economies of scale' has already been quoted, though many economists still tend to underestimate them. The old idea, that economies of scale could only work through the construction of excessively large individual industrial plants, has long been discredited. The 'economies of scale' are obtained in a more subtle manner, through the progressive specialization and subdivision of industrial processes, with sometimes an actual reduction in the average size of industrial plant. They also take effect through the existence of 'indivisibilities'. There are many costly economic provisions which a country needs whether its population is large or small, growing or stationary, whether we consider the very largest, such as the national transport system, public buildings or the provision of certain specialized types of industrial plant. We can observe the economic burden, in the early stages of growth, of providing these 'indivisibilities', calling for a marked increase in the proportion of the national product saved. But, as population and productivity grow, a country reaches a point where the 'capital/output ratio' (the average stock of capital required to produce each unit of product) actually begins to decline. For the U.S.A. and Britain, this occurred a hundred years ago or more; for Japan in the 1920s; India may be coming close to it now. Once any of these 'indivisibilities' has been provided, then further growth of population enables a country to 'spread its overheads', as a business man would put it. Under these circumstances, population growth is highly advantageous economically. The problem of securing sufficient capital investment to make economic development possible, in a poor country with a rapidly growing population, can for a time be very serious; but, for the reasons given above, it is not permanent. Economic aid from abroad (which Britain and Japan did not receive) may help other countries to get through the initial stages of development more rapidly and less painfully.

There have been many simple-minded calculations showing that a country will have to save an impossibly large proportion of its national product if it is to equip a population increase at the rate of 2 per cent per annum or more. Such calculations are, in the first instance, usually based on excessively high estimates of the capital/output ratio. But in addition, they suffer from the further grave fault of assuming that the marginal capital/output ratio, required to provide for an increase in product, is the same as the average ratio for existing production. This will almost certainly not be the case.

Population growth can thus in some cases actually reduce the demand for capital per unit of product. We see some of the most obvious examples of this in transport, where very high capital investment is needed when we have a sparse population spread out over a large area, while the converse prevails in a densely populated country.

But, in addition, it has recently been shown that population increase actually increases a country's supply of savings. This result is certainly paradoxical. Once again, people tend to consider it as an extension of the problem of the individual family. If more children are born, the parents find it harder to save. But this is not looking at the issue on a sufficiently long time scale. It must be remembered that a rapidly growing population will contain a high proportion of young men in their most economically productive years, when they are most capable of saving, and a low proportion of old people, drawing on past savings; while in a stationary or declining population, this situation will be reversed. This positive relationship between savings and population growth has been recently demonstrated by both theoretical and practical evidence. The most concrete evidence of all relates to India, where the rate of net saving as a percentage of net national product, calculated by the Reserve Bank of India (a highly objective authority) has risen from 5 per cent in the early 1950s to over 9 per cent in the early 1960s.

Bibliography

DEMOGRAPHY OF POPULATIONS IN 'ECOLOGICAL EQUILIBRIUM'

Ardener, E., *Divorce and Fertility*, Oxford University Press.
Glass, D., and Eversley, D. E. C. (eds.), *Population in History* (Essays in Historical Demography), Edward Arnold, 1965.

Russell, J. C., *British Medieval Population*, 1948.

Wrigley, E. A., *Introduction to English Historical Demography from the Sixteenth to the Nineteenth Century*, Weidenfeld & Nicolson, 1966.

ECONOMIC AND SOCIAL IMPLICATIONS
OF POPULATION CONTROL

Buguet, L., *L'optimum de population*, 1956.

Clark, C., *Population Growth and Land Use*, Macmillan, 1967.

Eversley, D. E. C., *Social Theories of Fertility and the Malthusian Debate*, Oxford University Press, 1959.

McCleary, G. F., *The Malthusian Population Theory*, Faber & Faber.

Sauvy, A., *Fertility and Survival*, Chatto & Windus, 1961.

Sauvy, A., *Richesse et Population*, 1943.

Sauvy, A., *Théorie Générale de la population (1952–4)*, 1956.

Notes on Contributors

ANTHONY ALLISON, is head of the Cell Pathology Division of the Clinical Research Centre temporarily at the National Institute for Medical Research, and has been a member of the Medical Research Council staff for most of his professional life. His interests range widely from population genetics to mechanisms of resistance against infections and tumours. He has edited the biology section of the Penguin Science Survey for 1966, 1967 and 1968.

DR ROSEMARY REID is a lecturer in zoology, specializing in the biology of water pollution problems, at Chelsea College of Science and Technology. She is interested in the use of audio-visual aids in teaching biology.

JOHN LANDER HARPER was Professor of Agriculture and Botany, and Head of the School of Plant Biology at the University College of North Wales, Bangor, until 1968. He is author of various publications on plant competition, plant population dynamics and the biology of weeds.

H. G. ANDREWARTHA is Professor of Zoology at the University of Adelaide. His publications, which include a number of technical papers in scientific journals and two books, *Introduction to the Study of Animal Populations* and (with L. C. Birch) *The Distribution and Abundance of Animals*, have been chiefly about population ecology, with minor excursions into the field of insect physiology.

CHRISTOPHER PERRINS is Senior Research Officer at the Edward Grey Institute of Field Ornithology. His work has been mainly on breeding biology and population studies, primarily with a long-term study of the Great Tit, but also with studies on the Mute Swan and the Swift.

LESLIE BROWN is an ex-civil servant now living on his wits. He has been a freelance author/consultant since 1963, carrying out short-term jobs for U.N.E.S.C.O., the World Bank, etc. He has been interested in birds all his life, and has written books on eagles, flamingoes (he has appeared twice on the TV. programme *Look* with flamingoes), the world's birds of prey, and a natural history of Africa, as well as contributing many scientific papers and articles for the popular press.

JOHN B. CALHOUN founded and heads the Unit for Research on Behavioral Systems (U.R.B.S.) in Maryland, U.S.A. This organization focuses on designing environments, re-identity formation, population growth, social withdrawal, and value formation and change.

W. BRASS is Reader in Medical Demography at the London School of Hygiene and Tropical Medicine. In 1961-2 he worked at Princeton University, U.S.A., on a study which resulted in the book *The Demography of Tropical Africa*, and he has been for shorter periods on projects in West Africa and Australia. His main research has been on methods for the collection and analysis of data on population, fertility and mortality in statistically underdeveloped areas.

ESTER BOSERUP, a Danish economist, has spent more than ten years on research into the problems of economic development for the United Nations, and has acted as economic consultant to other international bodies. Now a freelance author and research worker in Denmark, she has also written *The Conditions of Agricultural Growth* (1965), and *Woman's Role in Economic Development* (1970).

BURTON BENEDICT is Professor of Anthropology at the University of California, Berkeley. His principal publications are *Indians in a Plural Society*, *People of the Seychelles* and *Mauritius: Problems of a Plural Society*. He is also the editor of *Problems of Smaller Territories*. He was a member of the Royal Society Population Study Group from its founding in 1965 until he left England in 1968.

RUTH E. FOWLER, now in the Physiological Laboratory in Cambridge, gained an Honours degree in Genetics at the University of Edinburgh and a Ph.D. while she was assistant lecturer at the Institute of Animal Genetics. She married R. G. Edwards in 1956, and they have five children.

R. G. EDWARDS took a Diploma in Animal Genetics at Edinburgh University, where he also gained his Ph.D. Since then he has been actively engaged on research in genetics and reproductive physiology, first in Edinburgh and then at the National Institute for Medical Research at Mill Hill. Since 1963 he has been in the Physiology Department in Cambridge, and is currently working on the problems associated with mammalian and human development.

COLIN M. STEWART is a Principal Actuary in the Government Actuary's Department, where his official duties have included population analysis and projection as a basis for the financing of social security schemes. He is the author of a number of articles on this and related subjects, such as the analysis of statistics relating to fertility, and the demographic factors affecting the employment of married women. He was an active participant at the international population conferences in Belgrade (1950), Strasburg (1966) and London (1969).

COLIN CLARK is Director of the Institute for Research in Agricultural Economics at Oxford, a Professorial Fellow of Brasenose College, Oxford, and a Fellow of the Econometric Society. He is the author of a number of publications, his most recent being *Taxmanship* (with Miss M. R. Hasewell), *The Economics of Subsistence Agriculture* (revised editions 1966 and 1968), *Economics of Irrigation,* and *Population Growth and Land Use.* He has also contributed pamphlets and numerous articles to economics periodicals.